FOREWORD

List of Contributors
We would like to thank the following people for their contribution to this book.

Ron Cooper	Certification Manager, Royal Institute of Public Health & Hygiene	Chap 4 & Technical Editing
Les Raithby	Managing Director, Power Cleen Ltd.	Chap 7
Mathew Thompson	Technical Support Manager, MD associates Ltd.	Chap 7 & 8
Shaun Hannah	Software Director, MD associates Ltd.	Chap 8
David Worthington	Deputy Chief Environmental Health Advisor Welsh Office	Chap 10

We would also like to acknowledge the role of the following people from participating organisations:

Paul Brady & Samir Patel	Biotrace
Zoe Fearn	University of Wales Institute Cardiff
Jan Harrison	MD associates

Contributions from Associated Research Projects

We would also like to recognise:

Grimsby Europe's Food Town - Sanitation Benchmarking.

UK Department for International Development (DFID) in supporting research into cost effective cleaning (project No. R6959).

United Nations Food and Agricultural Organisation (F.A.O.) Economic Engineering Team led by Hector Lupin and coordinated by Ib Kollavik-Jensen.

The Canadian Food Inspection Agency (C.F.I.A.) Team led by Vance McEachern and involving Sharon Flack, Paul Fahie, Ed Verreth, Lyman Caines, Pete Arnfield, Richard Garriock, Bob Cramm and Taras Melynk.

Finally we acknowledge the role of Spencer Garrett who has both encouraged our team and provided practical information on the cost of food control systems.

FOREWORD

Internationally, food poisoning and its prevention is a high priority. Recent years have seen the emergence of new pathogens and very large scale outbreaks of food poisoning. Some of the pathogens of increasing concern have a very low minimum infective dose and this makes cleaning and the prevention of cross contamination even more important.

Part of the international response has been the introduction of food safety management systems based upon HACCP and readers are referred to previous books in the "How To" series. One control measure in many HACCP plans may be the cleanliness of surfaces especially those in contact with foods that are ready to eat. It is therefore surprising that in many food premises cleaning is of a low priority with often the most poorly paid and poorly trained staff performing the cleaning. It is in response to their needs as well as others in managing food operations that this book has been produced.

Chapter 1 presents an overview to cleaning and should be read first. Thereafter individual chapters can be read in any order and deal with specific aspects of cleaning in more detail.

Each chapter attempts to both describe and explain aspects of cleaning. The understanding is important, if people understand the principles of what they are doing they are more likely to implement cleaning properly. They are also more likely to be self-sufficient and be capable of making informed decisions for themselves.

A number of terms, words and definitions to describe cleaning are widely used in the food industry although the precise meaning of these terms is not universally agreed. Variations in interpretation occur within different sectors of the industry, between catering and manufacturing, between different manufacturers of cleaning materials and between different countries and continents. The terms in this book are the most widely accepted within the UK.

GRIMSBY EUROPE'S FOOD TOWN

MDA are situated in the European Food Town of Grimsby. The company take an active part in supporting local industry information needs through the provision of their "How to " range of books. This is the third book in the series and focuses on the increasing importance of cleaning. The company is a member of the "Food Town" executive committee and are happy to promote the benefits of Food Town within the introduction to this text.

Grimsby situated midway along the Eastern seaboard of the UK has an unrivalled history as a fishing port and centre of food production. Its strategic position just a short crossing from the major European markets has resulted in the commercial ports of Grimsby and Immingham becoming the largest in foreign trade terms in the UK.

The development of the food sector in the area has led to the organic growth of a self - sustaining food manufacturing and food industry service community. This ensures that local supplier's can meet the needs of food manufacturing companies, 24 hours a day 365 days a year. Whether it is refrigeration, processing equipment, general engineering, cleaning or research and development services that are required Food Town delivers.

FoodTown boasts the largest concentration of cold storage facilities in the UK with over 1.3 million cubic metres of private and public cold stores. Food Town distribution companies ensure that ambient, chilled and frozen transport services are available throughout the UK and Europe. Fish is still vital to the local economy with Grimsby home to approximately 20% of the UK industry but the vegetable processing industry is also well represented, as is the production of ready meals, Food Town is also home to Europe's largest pizza production facility.

The Food Town campaign is directed by a local government/industry partnership, which is keen to ensure that Food Town, and its companies remain competitive and market leaders in their fields. If your company is interested in accessing the European or UK markets or would like to learn more about what Food Town can offer, you now have the opportunity.

Contact Food Town at the following website: www.foodtown.co.uk
Telephone: ++ 44 (0) 1472 324619   Fax: ++ 44 (0) 1472 325955

Councillor Stephen J. Norton
Chair of North East Lincolnshire Council
Economic & Tourism Development Committee

Chapter 1. INTRODUCTION

1.1 What is Cleaning?

Cleaning is the removal of "soil" from surfaces and is of particular importance when the surfaces may directly or indirectly come into contact with food. "Soil" can be described as "matter out of place" and may be of organic or inorganic origin. In the food industry the organic components are most usually of food origin, (see 2.1) with or without associated microorganisms. The adequacy of cleaning may become critical if the food is likely to be eaten without further processing or cooking. The term "soil" has become, under some circumstances, synonomous with dirt.

How cleaning is carried out will depend upon the type and amount of soil present, the type of surface to be cleaned, the materials to be used (including water quality) and the standard of cleanliness required. As these are likely to differ considerably between food operations there is no one single right way to clean.

1.2 Why Clean?

Cleaning is important to the food industry for many reasons but of paramount importance is its contribution to product safety and shelf life. Because of its contribution to product safety it is a legal requirement that "all articles, fittings and equipment with which food comes into contact shall be kept clean" (see 10.1). A further requirement is that they should be designed and constructed to allow easy cleaning and maintained in good condition and repair. Equipment properly designed, constructed and cleaned presents a minimum contamination risk to foods from microorganisms or foreign bodies. Guidance on how to comply with legislation is contained in the various industry guides.

Cleaning and clean premises are important for other reasons. They display to auditors and staff that the company has a commitment to food hygiene as well as contributing to a pleasant work environment. Well-cleaned equipment and plant set standards for other areas of food hygiene. The visible cleanliness of a food operation is often the first thing to be noticed by auditors, inspectors, environmental health officers and even customers. Remember, "you only have one chance to make a first impression" and the company's success and profitability may depend upon its cleanliness.

Cleaning and the management of cleaning are of considerable economic importance. Build up of food residue can attract pests, increase maintenance costs, reduce the efficiency and life span of equipment and increase product wastage. However staff time, and chemicals etc., used in cleaning cost money. Increasingly the food control costs within a business need to be justified and managed. It therefore makes good business sense for management to calculate and optimise the costs associated with cleaning and to ensure what they are doing is effective and offers good value for money. At the same time the type of "soil" or waste being cleaned or removed should be reviewed with the aim of minimising waste and disposing of it safely and effectively.

It is for these reasons, as well as food safety, that cleaning and disinfection have become essential to the running of food operations

1.3 Cleaning, Disinfecting and Sanitising

Cleaning was defined (1.1) as the removal of soil or dirt and should result in a visibly clean surface, visibly free from food product, food residue, dirt, grease, etc. This level or degree of cleanliness may be sufficient for some areas of a food business however, visibly clean surfaces may not be free from microorganisms. Cleaning removes food residue and in doing so removes some of the microbial flora as well as reducing opportunities for any microorganisms present to grow and multiply. However surfaces in contact with food, to minimise contamination, must have a low residual level of microorganisms. In such cases, after cleaning, an additional disinfection stage is often required. Disinfection is the destruction or removal of microorganisms. It is unlikely that all microorganisms will be destroyed, even if they were, re-contamination e.g. from the air is likely to occur relatively quickly. The aim of disinfection is to reduce the number of microorganisms to a level which poses no risk to health or product quality. Thus the number of microorganisms has been reduced to an acceptable level for that area. Disinfection can be achieved by heat or chemicals and for maximum efficiency usually takes place after cleaning, hence the phrase 'terminal disinfection'. Cleaning and disinfection are therefore technically different although both may reduce the number of contaminant microorganisms. Cleaning may be undertaken without disinfection. Disinfection however, should never be undertaken on heavily soiled surfaces as the soil will reduce the efficiency of any disinfectants used. An alternative is sanitising. Within the UK sanitising is a cleaning process, for equipment or premises, which incorporates an element of disinfection. This process is achieved by using a sanitiser a combined detergent-disinfectant. In practice sanitising is usually less effective than separate cleaning and disinfection stages and traditionally would be used in low soil areas of a food plant.

It should be noted that in the USA the term sanitation is much broader and includes elements of hygiene or "any conditions favourable to good health". The term sanitise being equivalent to disinfection. Sometimes the terms sterilising and sterilant are used they are however misnomers. Sterile surfaces are normally not required or achievable in the food industry.

1.4 Principles of Cleaning

The objective of cleaning is to ensure that a surface or object is free from undesirable chemical, physical or microbiological contamination. Food residue, microorganisms, dirt and grease, etc. may firmly adhere to the surface and energy must be applied to remove them. The energy is applied in a series of steps or stages and may be kinetic, chemical or thermal. Any one of the stages in cleaning usually uses a combination of two or more forms of energy.

1.4.1 Application of Energy

Kinetic (mechanical) energy deals with movement or motion and can be generated manually in the form of hand scrubbing ("elbow grease") or by liquid flow or by using machines. Mechanical scrubbing devices are especially useful on floors and other large surface areas requiring prolonged application times. Mechanical energy is also generated from liquid flow and turbulence in cleaning in place (CIP) systems. Any economic and effective cleaning programme is a judicious balance of the various forms of energy (see Fig.1.1). The application of kinetic/mechanical energy may be particularly useful in the removal of biofilms.

Table 1.1 Typical Stages in a Food Surface Cleaning Programme

STAGE	FUNCTION	REASON
1 Pre-clean	Remove loose food or dirt, scrape, vacuum, etc.	Improves efficiency of later stages, allows detergent access to more firmly adhering residues
2 Main clean	Removes more firmly adhering food residue, grease or dirt. Usually detergents used to emulsify food particles and reduce surface tension.	Improves efficiency of later stages. Presence of dirt / residue / grease reduces the efficiency of disinfectants.
3 Rinse	Removes detergent & emulsified / dissolved dirt and grease	Improves efficiency of disinfection, minimises any reactions between cleaning chemicals
4 Disinfect	Further reduction in the number of microorganisms	Minimises risk of cross contamination increases product shelf life and safety
5 Final Rinse	Removes traces of disinfectant	Minimises risk of disinfectant contaminating the food.
6 Dry	Air dry or use disposable materials to minimise recontamination	Residual moisture provides an opportunity for any remaining microorganisms to grow and survive and increases the risk of cross contamination.

Fig 1.1 Relative Energy and Time Components of some Different Cleaning Programmes

Generalised Cleaning Programme

Cleaning floor with a machine

Manual Clean of Work Surface

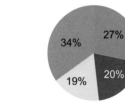

Soaking equipment in a sink / soak tank

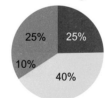

Foam Cleaning

Low Temperature Cleaning

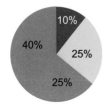

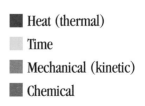

■ Heat (thermal)
▢ Time
▨ Mechanical (kinetic)
■ Chemical

1.4.2 Stages in Cleaning

The aims of cleaning are to remove the dirt/residues/microorganisms from the surface, maintain these residues in suspension (prevent re-deposition) and finally remove the suspended residues from the surface. If additional disinfection is required this takes place after the removal of the food soil.

The precise number of steps or stages required to achieve these aims will vary depending upon circumstances but typical programmes contain 6 stages and these are outlined in Table 1.1. Not all of these steps are always required and will vary depending upon surface use and the level of risk as well as the frequency of cleaning. For example a lightly soiled surface of low risk may not need a pre-clean or a disinfection stage. The use of a sanitiser may combine stages 2 and 4. Alternatively additional stages e.g. a rinse between stages 1 and 2 can be added to maximise efficiency, for example on surfaces which carry a high level of relatively loosely bound food particles e.g. meat in processing plants. However it is important that the order of the stages in cleaning should not be changed.

The importance of removing gross soil / loosely adhering food debris cannot be over-emphasised. The application of usually mechanical energy, at an early stage, can increase the likelihood of success of the later stages. Care should be taken that mechanical means of removing gross soil (brushes, scrapers, etc.) do not damage the surface allowing dirt and microorganisms to become trapped.

Operatives, however, must be aware that surfaces free from gross debris may look "visually clean" but may be "microbiologically" and even "chemically" unacceptable.

1.5 When To Clean

When cleaning should take place depends upon the level of risk posed and the rate of product and microbial build up in relation to production patterns. Cleaning frequency should not be a matter of guesswork but should be arrived at scientifically.

In many instances, especially in catering, retailing and similar food manufacturing operations "clean as you go" is both practicable and desirable. As soon as a surface has been used for a task it is cleaned before being used for anything else. This both minimises the risk of cross contamination and makes cleaning at the end of the day much easier. Product accumulation on a heavily used surface in one working day may be difficult to remove. Good practices associated with "clean as you go" are the removal of waste and rubbish and keeping surfaces free from unnecessary clutter or equipment. At the end of the working day, all areas receive a "final clean".

In larger manufacturing operations "clean as you go" is not possible and cleaning takes place at the end of the shift (typically 8 hours) although some production units run continuously for two shifts. The acceptability of this should be determined by surface testing (chapter 6) and by monitoring the microbiological quality of the end product. The microbial quality of a product produced at the end of a shift should be as good as that produced at the beginning. If product residue and microorganisms are left to build up for too long this will not be the case.

1.6 Resources Used in Cleaning

Resources used in cleaning can be classified as human, chemical and physical. Human resources are often the most expensive and require appropriate training. Chemical resources need to be carefully selected to ensure they are safe, compatible with other chemicals used and capable of achieving, within time / temperature constraints, an appropriate level of surface cleanliness. This is subject to their correct use within Health and Safety guidelines. Physical resources (cleaning equipment) should be clean as well as easily cleaned and disinfected. Increasingly colour coding is essential to ensure that equipment, used to clean areas where raw materials are handled, are not used to clean areas where finished products may be present. Equipment used in cleaning is often a "forgotten component" of a successful cleaning programme and should be in good repair and replaced when worn or when it can no longer be cleaned effectively.

Table 1.2 Chemical and Physical Resources Used in Cleaning

Chemical - Sources of chemical energy
Detergents — remove dirt, grease and food residue   Disinfectants - destroy microorganisms   Sanitiser — combined detergent / disinfectant
Physical - Application of physical and chemical energy
Cleaning cloths, brushes, cleaning machines, power washers, steam cleaners, vacuum pick-ups, sprays, lances, etc.

1.7 Management of Cleaning

Current estimates suggest that the UK food industry spends over £800 million pounds on cleaning. To ensure this money is spent wisely and effectively requires good management. It is therefore surprising that people involved in cleaning are usually not well paid, often poorly motivated and supervised, with cleaning often ineffectively monitored.

The foundations for a successful cleaning programme are laid in the correct design and construction of premises and plant. Cleaning must be accepted by senior management as important, requiring appropriate resources, and not regarded merely as a routine process, performed with little knowledge of what is actually required and achievable.

One of the major management decisions to be taken is whether to clean "in house" or "contract out". Cleaning in house allows better control of costs and standards but must not be viewed as an activity to be targeted in a cost cutting exercise. Contract cleaning companies will argue that food companies can benefit from their specialist knowledge. However, using outside contractors does not absolve the company from its responsibility to ensure they have clean plant. The use of cleaning related computer software can aid the management process as can the use of independent cleaning auditors. Proper cleaning management requires a correctly constructed, implemented and monitored cleaning programme. Data from monitoring should be retained and used in trend analysis and compared to benchmark values obtained when the cleaning programme was validated. (See 8.5). It will also aid, if necessary, the construction of a due diligence defence.

1.7.1 Hygieneomics

Nineteen ninety nine saw the launch of the Hygieneomics Initiative. This concept involves the integration of all aspects of food safety and cleaning, as well as all other aspects of running a business, into one management system. Food safety and cleaning are not viewed as "add ons" to management but as central strands of the company's whole management philosophy. This approach uses cost benefit data to show that food safety and cleaning are the hallmarks of a successful business and has the ambition of setting a global hygiene standard. Further information can be obtained from the hygieneomics web site (Armstrong, 1999).

The increasing importance of controlling and cleaning costs is reflected in the recent publication of a specific best practice guide (ETBPP, 1998).

1.8 Novel Methods of Cleaning

New approaches to cleaning are being examined in an attempt to make cleaning easier, more effective and cost efficient. Two examples include the use of ultrasound and solid CO_2 (cryogenic) cleaning.

In ultrasound, which can be used in conjunction with chemical cleaners and hot (60-70°C) water, microscopic bubbles are produced which release energy (known as cavitation) and help to remove "soil" from the surfaces of small items of equipment. It tends to be noisy and expensive but useful for some smaller delicate items.

Cryogenic cleaning uses mechanical energy (turbulence) caused by the expansion of dry ice which dislodges soil. The solid CO_2 is applied as a fine spray in clean dry air (see 3.4).

Whatever method is used, including novel methods, it should form part of a monitored, documented cleaning schedule.

1.9 Cleaning and HACCP

HACCP is both a food safety risk-based management system as well as a philosophy. It provides a set of guidelines on how to produce safe food and HACCP or HACCP-based approaches are increasingly being required within national legislation. In constructing a HACCP plan the HACCP team will identify hazards associated with their product(s) and how they can be controlled at critical points using specified control measures. This approach is especially important for foods that are eaten by the consumer without any further processing or heating. For example, tanks / pipework through which pasteurised milk passes are likely to be designated critical control points with cleaning a control measure to avoid post pasteurisation contamination. Similarly surfaces in contact with cooked meats, salads, etc. are likely to be designated as critical control points. This does not mean that cleaning of others areas can be ignored. HACCP cannot work in isolation and depends for its success upon a range of supporting hygiene practices. These have variously been called Pre Requisite Programmes (PRPs), Good Hygiene Practice (GHP), etc. Cleaning therefore is vital at all stages in handling / processing food with a dual emphasis on preventing contamination of the food and preventing raw materials contaminating the premises, plant, equipment, people and other foods.

Chapter 2. TYPES OF SOIL

2.1 Chemical Components of Soil

Soiling is a natural process that occurs in all food plants, the extent and nature depending upon the food and processing involved. An understanding of soil composition and chemistry in a food operation is important in designing an appropriate cleaning programme. Additional factors to consider are:

- what effect heat will have on the soil?
- where exactly is the soil building up?
- what is the level of soil?
- how easy is the soil to remove? (See Table 2.1).

Soil can vary in its chemical and microbiological composition depending upon age, environmental factors such as temperature and the position in the production process (see Fig 2.1). Chemically, soil is a blend of minerals, fats, carbohydrates and proteins which, depending upon their molecular size and charge may or may not be soluble in water (see Fig 2.2). Heat can affect the soil for example caramelising sugars or denaturing proteins, and these changes may make the soil more difficult to remove. The main determinant (see 2.2) of the soil chemistry is the type of food residue present, thus for example, meat soil tends to have a higher fat content whilst cereal soil a higher carbohydrate content.

Table 2.1 Removability of Various Food Soils

FOOD SOIL	REMOVABILITY
High water content, acidic, e.g. fruit, vegetable soil	Easy to remove
Higher starch, protein, fat content plus vegetable matter to remove	Moderately difficult
Protein, fat with meat / melted cheese	Difficult to remove

Fig. 2.1 Variation in some Chemical Components of Milk Soil in Different Processing Equipment

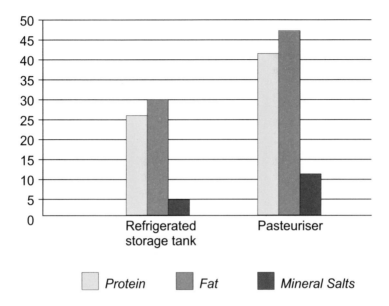

The type and form (e.g. liquid, solid, semi solid) of the soil determines the type of chemicals to be used in cleaning. These along with heat energy cause chemical changes in the soil which should help in its removal (see Table 2.1).

Fig. 2.2 Solubility of Soil Components in Water

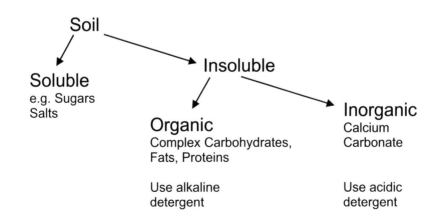

2.2 Formation, Origin and Removal of Soil

The most important sources of food soil, including any contaminating microorganisms are raw materials. These can be augmented from a range of other sources (see 2.2.2-2.2.4). If cleaning and disinfection are poor then surface contamination can build up, especially in inaccessable places, and act as a source of product contamination. An important part in managing cleaning is to <u>minimise</u> the build up of soil i.e. prevention rather than cure. Cause and effect analysis can be used to both identify ways in which soil builds up as well as to seek remedies to faults in the cleaning itself (see Appendix 2).

2.2.1 Raw Materials

Raw materials entering a plant should be in as clean a condition as possible e.g. root vegetables should be free from soil, animal hides free from excrement. Careful handling and disposal of raw material containers / packaging is important to prevent clutter, minimise waste accumulation and reduce the risk of pest problems.

Table 2.2 Pests as a Source of Contamination

PEST	ORGANIC CONTAMINANT	ROUTE OF MICROBIAL CONTAMINATION
Cockroach	Moult cases, faeces, dead bodies	Mechanical transfer from feet directly or indirectly from faeces
Birds	Feathers, droppings, dead bodies	Mechanical transfer from feet directly or indirectly from faeces
Flies	Droppings, dead bodies regurgitation	Mechanical transfer from feet directly /indirectly from faeces or regurgitation
Rat / Mouse	Droppings, dead bodies, urine saliva	Mechanical transfer from feet directly or indirectly from faeces or saliva

2.2.2 Pests

Different types of pests can contaminate food / food surfaces with microorganisms and with organic matter. (See Table 2.2).

2.2.3 Humans

Humans can act as a source of microorganisms and organic matter. Dead skin cells, which may also carry microorganisms are a major constituent of dust. Humans can also contribute to the microbial flora of the air and surfaces via hands, hair, breathing and clothing, hence the need for strict standards of personal hygiene.

2.2.4 Air

The microbiology of the air found in food processing plants and methods for controlling it are attracting increasing attention. Microorganisms in the air can exist in spore form especially mould spores in a dusty environment or in aerosols as well as aerial dispersions of free vegetative microorganisms. They can also be attached to dust particles or water droplets. Smaller particles (less than about 2µm) tend to remain suspended in the air, whilst larger particles drop to the ground quite quickly. Ideally the air in high risk food manufacturing premises should be filtered or treated (e.g. ozone) to reduce microbial contamination.

Table 2.3
Sources of Microorganisms in the Air and Methods for Minimising Contamination

SOURCE	PREVENTION
Outside Air	Unbroken, well fitting windows and doors, air locks, filtration of air supplies, positive pressure
Ventilation / Air Conditioning	Ventilation systems can act as breeding grounds for some organisms. The use of filters and proper cleaning, maintenance and temperature control are important.
Processes (including cleaning)	Minimise generation of aerosols, containment of areas where aerosols are generated.
People	Good personal hygiene, if appropriate snoods, face masks, protective clothing, hair nets, etc. are worn.
Drains	Do not clean with pressure jets this can re-contaminate surfaces and result in atmospheric contamination.
Others Sources:	UV Light - Bactericidal, needs careful positioning, poor penetrating power. Fogging: Disinfectant mists. Ozonation - Use of ozone to disinfect and de-odourise.

2.2.5 Removal of Soil

Soil is difficult to remove from cracks, grooves or gaps in surfaces, especially if the surfaces are uneven, porous and difficult to access. Soil is most easily removed from smooth, joint free, hard, impervious surfaces. There are three basic steps in the removal of the soil i.e. separating the soil from the surface, dispersing the soil in solution and the prevention of re-deposition and attachment of the dispersed soil.

Mechanical, chemical and thermal energy applied to the soiled surfaces helps to break down the chemical bonds attaching the soil to the surface. The same three forms of energy also help to keep the soil dispersed in the cleaning solutions e.g. shaking in hot water with detergent.

2.3 Biofilms

So far the contamination of surfaces has been considered under the separate headings of chemical soil and microbial contamination. This distinction has some merit because of the two component activities that make up cleaning i.e. removing soil and destruction of microorganisms. It is possible, although unlikely in the food industry, to have chemical soil with no microbial contamination. However on many contact surfaces, these two components are often intimately interconnected in the formation of biofilms.

Microorganisms on a clean surface may arise fom a chance contamination and may be removed in a short space of time. Alternatively they can form a complex ecosystem known as a biofilm. There is no universally accepted definition of a biofilm but generally they consist of microorganisms, surrounded by moisture and chemical material, forming a matrix, adhering to the surface. Dental plaque consists of a biofilm which can be felt by the tongue, especially after long periods of non-cleaning, combined with eating It may accumulate to such a degree as to be visible. Studies have shown that biofilms can form on the majority of surfaces used in food premises and may vary in thickness from monolayers to layers 300µm thick with over 10^7 organisms /cm^2.

The formation of a biofilm (see Fig 2.3) starts with the conditioning (addition of a chemical coating) of the surface. New stainless steel is more difficult to condition and subsequently colonise than older, used stainless steel. Microbial cells land on the conditioned surface and then subsequently adhere and attach to it. The attached cells multiply and synthesise extracellular polymers often in quite large quantities (dental plaque high in polysaccaride is more pronounced on the teeth of people with a high sugar diet). The polymers along with water form a matrix (typically 98% water) which in turn can trap or bind particles, other bacteria or minerals. If left undisturbed, a complex microbial ecosystem, often consisting of many different species of microorganisms, may be formed. There is likely to be a two way interaction of gain and loss of microorganisms to the planktonic phase (region surrounding the biofilm). This loss is of importance as the organisms can be transferred to food or liquid passing over the biofilm. Of additional concern is that attached bacteria may be up to 1000 times less sensitive to disinfectants than free cells either because of the protective effect of the extra-cellular polymeric matrix or as part of a general stress response.

Biofilms are currently the focus of research and are important for the following reasons:-

- Can be a source of food spoilage organisms
- Can be source of food poisoning organisms
- Microorganisms in Biofilms are protected from UV light, disinfectants, starvation, heat, dessication.
- Can reduce heat transfer across surfaces
- Can lead to blockages in pipework

Fig. 2.3 Development of Biofilm (see Appendix 1)

Stage	Time scale
A - deposition of a conditioning film	seconds
B - adhesion of planktonic cells	minutes
C - cell division and further attachment	hours
D - formation of micro-colonies	hours
E - development of a mature biofilm	days

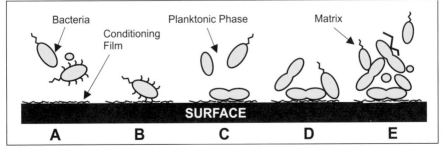

Source adapted from Ref. 7

Table 2.4 Some Pathogens Able to Form Biofilms

ORGANISM	ENVIRONMENT AT -RISK
Listeria monocytogenes	dairy, meat, poultry RTEM*
Salmonella spp.	dairy, meat, poultry
Campylobacter spp.	poultry
Staphylococcus aureus	poultry
Escherichia coli 0157	dairy, meat

*RTEM = Ready to eat meals

Table 2.5 illustrates some of the pathogens with biofilm forming abilities. Whilst most microorganisms are capable of some form of attachment and proliferation certain species have a particular aptitude. Psychrotrophic, cold growing, organisms such as food spoilage, *Pseudomonas spp.* and potential pathogens such as *Listeria spp.* fall into this category, and can survive long periods in a biofilm. Normal cleaning and disinfection routines may only achieve about a 1 log reduction in the number of microbial surface contaminants in biofilms. Pressure sprays at 17 bar for 1 second incorporated into cleaning have been shown to achieve a 3 log reduction, with the optimal distance from the spray lance being 125 - 250mm. Because of cleaning difficulties, strategies should be developed to prevent biofilm formation, which is more likely in moist/wet conditions in the presence of ample nutrients and a source of microorganisms (Gibson et al, 1999). Environmental factors influencing biofilm formation are included in Table 2.5.

Table 2.5 Factors Influencing Biofilm Formation

FACTORS	CONTRIBUTION	PREVENTION
Time	Extensive biofilm formation is more likely if left undisturbed.	Ensure adequacy & frequency of cleaning is appropriate. Ensure access to all surfaces and correct design to facilitate cleaning
Soil	High carbohydrate or high protein soils can enhance formation of matrix	Make sure detergents and temperatures used in cleaning adequately remove the type of soil encountered.
Bacterial Population	Microbial components of the biofilm are influenced by types of microorganisms present and their physiological status.	Microbial specifications for raw materials should state maximum aerobic plate count (APC) and absence of pathogens. Ensure disinfection is adequately performed. Consider additional disinfection e.g. use of ozone.
Constructional Material	Even visually smooth surfaces can, under the microscope, be seen to offer crevices, cracks facilitating colonisation	Ensure surface finish is smooth joint free and in good state of repair. Ensure equipment used in cleaning does not damage surface finish
Humidity/Water Levels	Moisture is needed for microbial growth and contributes to matrix of biofilm	Good ventilation, ensure water, Water steam is not used unnecessarily. Ensure appropriate opportunity for drying.
pH	Most bacteria grow at neutral to slightly acid pH. pH can also influence likelihood of microorganisms sedimenting out.	Ensure removal of food soil. Use acid or alkaline detergents.

Chapter 3 WATER USED IN CLEANING

3.1 Water Quality

Water is the commonest component on Earth making up approximately two thirds of its surface. It also constitutes about three quarters of the human body. Few substances are completely insoluble in water, and it is sometimes described as the "universal solvent". Water therefore forms an important component of most cleaning programmes. However water is a poor wetting agent and is used in conjunction with detergents (see 4.1) to improve its cleaning properties.

Given the importance of water it is self evident that good quality water is needed (see Table 3.1) in cleaning and in most circumstances it is also a legal requirement. Important quality attributes of water are the levels of microbiological and chemical contaminants

Table 3.1 Suggested Chemical and Microbiological Targets for Water Used in Cleaning

Chemical	
Total Hardness (as $CaCO_3$)	<50ppm (parts per million)
Sodium Chloride	<100ppm
Free Chlorine	<1ppm
pH	6.5-7.5
Iron (as Fe)	<1ppm
Nitrates	<10ppm
Microbiological	
Aerobic Plate Count (APC) at 22°C and 37°C	No significant increase over that normally observed. Typical target may be less than 100cfu/ml
Total Coliforms	0 per 100ml
Faecal Coliforms	0 per 100ml
Sulphite reducing clostridia	0 per 100 ml
Yeasts	0 per 20ml

3.1.1 Chemical Water Quality

Tap water is not chemically pure and invariably contains dissolved chemicals. These will vary around the country depending upon the source. Those dissolved chemicals contributing to water hardness are probably of greatest importance in cleaning.

Water is described as hard when it will not readily form a lather when shaken with soap solutions. The hardness is caused by dissolved metallic ions, principally calcium and magnesium, which react with soap producing a scum. The principal salts causing hardness are calcium hydrogen carbonate, calcium carbonate, magnesium hydrogen carbonate, magnesium carbonate as well as calcium and magnesium sulphate. These salts dissolve in rain water as it percolates through the ground. Variations in soil composition in different parts of the country lead to differences in the degree of water hardness.

Waters are classified compared to their content of dissolved calcium and magnesium ions and these are expressed as parts per million (ppm) of calcium carbonate. (See Table 3.2).

Table 3.2 Water Classification

AREA	DESCRIPTION	LEVEL
Devon	Soft	<50ppm
Wales	Soft to Moderately Soft	50-100ppm
Berkshire	Moderate to Hard	100-200ppm
London	Very Hard	>200ppm

Hardness caused by calcium and magnesium bicarbonates are described as temporary hardness since it can be removed by boiling.

$$Ca(HCO_3)_2 \qquad CaCO_3 \quad + \quad H_2O \quad + \quad CO_2$$

Soluble Calcium Bicarbonate	Insoluble Calcium Carbonate	Water	Carbon Dioxide

The bicarbonates are converted to an insoluble precipitate of calcium or magnesium carbonate respectively, by boiling and can be seen as "furring up" in kettles. In contrast calcium and magnesium sulphates are not decomposed by boiling and their presence in water is termed permanent hardness. The problems associated with hardness of water and their effect on cleaning are summarised in Table 3.3.

"Water softening" processes remove hardness from water. The most widely used method of water softening involves an ion exchange system. This involves the exchange of "hardness ions" (calcium and magnesium) for sodium ions by passing the hard water through a column containing an ion exchange resin. The decision about how to soften water needs to be based upon the cause and degree of water hardness.

Table 3.3 Problems Associated with Hardness of Water

SYMPTOM / EFFECT	CAUSE
Scum Formation	The reaction of dissolved calcium and magnesium ions with soap produces an insoluble grey scum which is deposited on sinks or objects being washed.
Excessive Consumption	Scum formation uses up a large excess of soap / detergent before a reasonable lather is achieved. This wastes detergent and increases costs. Modern detergents may contain "builders" which remove calcium and magnesium ions.
Re-deposition	Calcium and magnesium salts cause flocculations- the dirt suspended in water is re-deposited on the cleaned surface. Suspending (anti-deposition) agents may be added to detergents.
Scaling	In boiling, temporary hardness is converted to insoluble carbonates which are precipitated onto heating elements as scale or "fur". Build up of the deposit on the element acts as an insulating layer and decreases the efficiency of the heat transfer. Scale may build up in pipework (e.g. CIP systems) and reduce water flow. Descaling agents may be added to water systems.

3.1.2 Microbiological Water Quality

Water used in cleaning must be "potable" i.e. suitable for human consumption. If non-potable water is used within a manufacturing plant then this should be clearly differentiated from the potable water and precautions taken so that it cannot be used in cleaning. There are special legal requirements relating to the use of non-potable water in food premises.

The microbiological quality of the water should be monitored at the point of use (not entry). It is possible for biofilms to form in pipework and significantly increase the microbial count in the water resulting in the application of contaminated water (high APC) to food surfaces.

The microbiological quality of water is of particular importance in the cleaning of high risk areas and water with a high aerobic plate count (APC) can contribute to decreased product shelf life. An additional concern is that contaminated water can be a health risk. Traditional concerns have concentrated on the presence of coliforms as indicator organisms, the original concept being that they indicated faecal pollution. Whilst the latter are still routinely tested for other organisms are also of concern. These include bacteria such a *Campylobacter* as well as protozoans such as *Giardia* and *Cryptosporidium*. The latter have been associated with waterborne outbreaks of disease and show some resistance to chlorination. Correct water filtration, at source, is important in prevention but both of these pathogens have a low minimum infective dose. Filters, able to remove *Cryptosporidium* from running water supplies are now available.

If the microbiological quality of water is considered critical then additional safety measures can be taken. These include UV or ozone treatments which can be used separately or in combination. Ozone bubbles exposed to UV light are said to form hydroxyl radicles with increased disinfection potential (see 4.2.9). Additional chlorination can also be used although this could pass on a taste to the product if used at too high a concentration.

3.2 Water in Cleaning

Water is a very poor wetting agent since it tends to remain as a drop even when placed on the surface (see Fig. 3.1). This is because water has a high surface tension. A drop of water is composed of innumerable molecules which are attracted to one another. In the body of the drop these intermolecular forces operate evenly in all directions. However at the surface of the water drop all the forces on the molecules are exerted inwards and between the surface molecules, pulling them into the body of the liquid. The surface area of the drop is reduced to a minimum and so it takes on a spherical shape. Objects, such as a needle, can be made to float on the surface of water as a result of surface tension (see Fig. 3.2).

How to Clean

Fig 3.1 Intermolecular Forces Acting In a Drop of Water

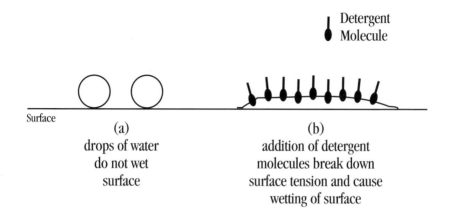

Detergent Molecule

Surface

(a)
drops of water
do not wet
surface

(b)
addition of detergent
molecules break down
surface tension and cause
wetting of surface

Fig 3.2 Intermolecular Forces at the Surface of Water are Sufficient to Allow Small Objects, e.g. Needle to be suspended.

Intermolecular forces
sufficiently strong to
form 'skin' on which
small objects can 'float'.

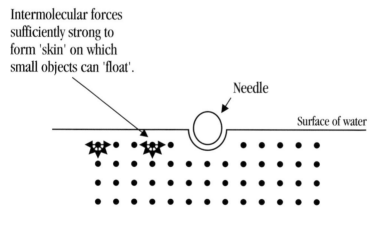

Needle

Surface of water

3.3 Water Temperature and Pressure
The use of water at elevated temperatures adds thermal energy and this can be useful for two reasons: to facilitate removal of soil and to disinfect i.e. destroy microorganisms.

3.3.1 Water Temperature
Typically a temperature increase of 10°C doubles the efficacy of a process but for most processes the optimum temperature will lie between 45-60°C. There is an oncost in

heating water and this should be considered when costing cleaning. Table 3.4 illustrates various temperatures and pressures which can be used in a typical cleaning programme. The temperature of water in cleaning needs to be appropriate for the type of soil present and cleaning process used. Too high a temperature can cause coagulation of protein and a greater tendency for it to adhere to surfaces. Too low a temperature and it may be more difficult to remove fat residues. Recently sanitisers have been developed especially formulated to be effective at lower temperatures e.g. 10°C.

Heat is a reliable and effective means of destroying microorganisms alone or in combination with chemical disinfectants although residual food soil will protect remaining microorganisms from heat or chemical disinfection. The destructive effect depends upon the heat energy absorbed by the microorganism and will be a function of temperature and time. For this reason disinfection by hot water should always state the target temperature and the length of exposure, with typically a temperature of 82°C for 1 minute being required. It should also be remembered that heat is lost very quickly from jets of water, approx 2°C for every 10cm distance, and large surface areas will quickly absorb and dissipate heat energy. It is the temperature of the water hitting the surface that is important, not the temperature leaving the nozzle. Also important is the initial temperature of the surface, this can cool the water down and the surfaces may need preheating for optimal effect.

Steam may sometimes be incorporated into the cleaning programme. This can have some advantages especially with ingrained fat deposits although steam is usually at a much lower pressure than heated water. Steam disinfection can also be used and whilst the equipment exposed to the steam is self drying, condensation elsewhere in the plant can be increased. Additionally steam can affect some types of equipment and plant finishes. Careless use of steam supplies moisture and warmth for microorganisms to grow.

More recently steam vapour systems have been designed to discharge penetrative dry steam at up to 180°C with 8 bar pressure. This results in very little condensation and is suitable for use in the presence of electrical equipment. This type of technique is particularly useful in bakeries for removing carbon and baked-on bread paste and for cleaning ovens.

3.3.2 Water Pressure
Water under pressure can be used in both cleaning out of place (COP) and cleaning in place (CIP) systems. In COP, water jets can be used to impart high kinetic energy and

have a number of advantages, including penetrating ability. However, care must be taken as the pressure sprays can be carelessly aimed and may transfer microorganisms and soil from one surface to another directly or via aerosols. Water under pressure may be useful in removing biofilm. (see 2.3)

Table 3.4 Use of Increased Water Temperature and Pressure in Cleaning

STAGE	WATER TEMPERATURE	WATER PRESSURE
Pre-cleaning Stage	Ambient (20°C)	Medium Pressure (30 bar)
Detergent / Soil Removal Rinse	40-50°C	Medium-High Pressure (30-60 bar)
Final Rinse	Ambient - High (20-82°C)	Medium Pressure (30 bar)

3.4 Dry Cleaning

Although water is a good solvent and forms the basis for most cleaning programmes there are occasions when it is better to minimise its use.

If the type of food debris accumulating on a surface is powdery or hygroscopic, or for some high fat products, then initial removal without the use of wetting is desirable. At its simplest this may include sweeping or "picking up" by hand. Sweeping can transfer soil and microorganisms from one place to another by air and a better alternative is to use a form of vacuuming.

In plants producing dry products e.g. flour, cereals, dried powders, the use of water should be minimised as it can impair product quality. In such circumstances vacuuming followed by the use of an alcohol sanitiser can be used. This evaporates from the surface quickly.

An alternative form of dry cleaning is to use non aggressive small dry ice pellets applied with force. These can remove sticky residues and baked on products without the need for solvents and have been recommended for cleaning equipment in contact with highly concentrated flavourings.

Chapter 4 CHEMICALS USED IN CLEANING

4.1 Detergents

4.1.1 Background

The term 'detergent' literally means 'something which cleans' and is likely to be formulated to perform a specific type of task (see Table 4.1).
Detergents can be classified as :-

- surfactant detergents,
- alkaline and acidic detergents,
- abrasive cleaners,
- solvents

4.1.2 Surfactant Detergents (See Fig 4.1.)

The term surfactant is a shortened form of surface active agent and these are detergents which act with water to cleanse by :

1. Reducing surface tension this allows water to wet the surface being cleaned (see 3.2)

2. Emulsifying greasy dirt, the hydrophobic tails of the detergent molecules bury themselves in the grease leaving the hydrophilic heads at the water-grease interface. The like charges of the hydrophilic heads repel each other and cause the grease to form suspended droplets in the cleaning solution. Surfactant molecules act as emulsifying agents since adding an aqueous detergent solution to grease produces two immiscible liquid phases, one dispersed in the other (see Fig 4.2.)

3. Suspending greasy dirty particles Surfactant molecules become associated with the cleaned surface as well as with the greasy dirt particles. Forces of repulsion between the heads of the surfactant molecules prevent the dirt particles flocculating and re-depositing themselves on the cleaned surface and so they remain suspended and can be rinsed away. Residual surfactant molecules on surfaces may be passed onto food and have been implicated in certain types of gut irritation. Rinsing may, therefore, be required after cleaning.

Fig. 4.1 A Schematic Representation of a Surfactant Molecule

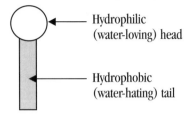

Hydrophilic
(water-loving) head

Hydrophobic
(water-hating) tail

Fig. 4.2 Emulsification of Grease by Surfactant Action

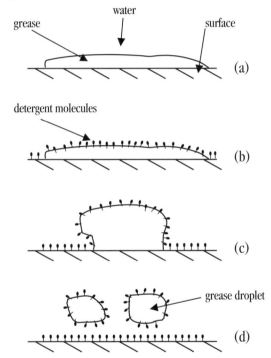

Fig 4.2. Emulsification of grease by surfactant action (a) grease does not dissolve even in hot water (b) addition of surfactant molecules cause hydrophilic heads to remain at grease water interface and hydrophobic tails to bury themselves in the grease (c) repulsion of hydrophilic heads roll up the grease (d) grease droplets become suspended and cannot coalesce or redeposit themselves on the surface due to repulsion between hydrophilic heads. Surfaces should be rinsed well after washing and before drying to remove surfactant molecules.

Table 4.1 Composition of a Soapless Washing Powder

FUNCTION	PROPERTY	EXAMPLES
Surfactant Detergent	Cleaning	Sodium alkyl benzene sulphonate
Builder	Soften water, suspend soil and improve cleaning	Sodium tripolyphosphate
Conditioner	Improves flow of Powder, maintains alkalinity, and protects metal machine parts	Anhydrous sodium silicate
Filler	Bulking agent, keeps granules crisp	Anhydrous sodium silicate
Bleaching Agent	Stain removal Sodium perborate	
Bleach Precursor	Enables bleach action to start at lower temperatures	Tetra acetyl ethylene diamine (TAED)
Anti-redeposition Agent	Helps suspend dirt particles	Sodium carboxy methyl cellulose
Foam Stabiliser	Improves lather	Ethanolamide
Fluorescing Agent	Improves whiteness	
Perfumes and Dyes	Increase consumer acceptability but can cause skin allergies	
Enzymes	Digest protein based stains	

4.1.3 Types of Surfactant Detergent

Surfactants are classified according to the charge carried on the hydrophilic head of the molecule. Anionic surfactants have a negatively charged hydrophilic head and cationic surfactants have a positively charged hydrophilic head. Ampholytic (amphoteric) surfactants can be either anionic or cationic according to the pH of their surroundings. Non-ionic surfactants do not ionise.

Anionic surfactants include the soaps (sodium stearate) and soap-less detergents (sodium alkyl benzene sulphonate). Soaps have a pH of 8-9 whereas soapless surfactants are neutral. Soaps are mainly used in hand washing and as soap flakes in washing powders for fabrics. Soaps help to lubricate the fabric fibres and maintain softness but are of limited value since they form a scum in hard water (see 3.1.1). Soapless surfactants are used in washing up liquids and, in combination with other ingredients, in a range of cleaners. Some produce large amounts of foam and the removal of this by rinsing can be a time-consuming problem.

Cationic surfactants are slightly acidic (pH 6 -7) and the most important are the quarternary ammonium compounds (quats). They have limited detergency power but possess anti-bacterial properties and can be used for disinfection. Quats have antistatic properties and are the best detergents for washing plastic glasses and tumblers since anionic surfactants produce clouding.

Ampholytic surfactants based on amino acids, are good emulsifiers and although possessing some bactericidal properties are relatively expensive and are used in medicated liquid soaps.

Non-ionic surfactants have good scum dispersing properties and can be used in conjunction with anionic surfactants to produce low-lather products which are particularly suitable for automatic washing machines and floor cleaning machines. They may be used with quaternary ammonium surfactants in sanitisers (see 4.3).

The choice of a particular detergent will depend on the application, one requirement being that products designed for hand cleaning should avoid components likely to cause allergic reactions. Some anionic surfactants e.g. sodium lauryl sulphate, can cause skin allergies as do some perfumes and dyes incorporated into soapless washing powders. Properties of the various types of surfactant detergents are summarised in Table 4.2. This table illustrates that all surfactants possess a hydrophobic tail but differ in the charge found on the hydrophilic head. Anionic surfactants have a negatively charged hand with cationic detergents being positively charged. Non-ionic detergents have a neutral head.

4.1.4 Incompatability of Anionic and Cationic Surfactants

Normally the mixing of an anionic and cationic surfactant and the attraction of their oppositely charged heads, results in the formation of complex insoluble products which are precipitated from solution and they loose their detergent effect. The production of a lather and roll up of grease depends upon repulsion of like charges. The mixing of anionic and cationic surfactants causes lather to collapse. Where an anionic and cationic product need to be used in the same place, the first product should be carefully rinsed away to ensure activity of the second e.g. hypochlorites must not be mixed with cationic detergents. A small number of cationic surfactants, e.g. benzalkonium succharinate, are compatible with anionic surfactants.

4.1.5 Alkaline and Acid Detergents (Cleaners)

Alkaline Detergents (Degreasing Agents) - Alkaline detergents vary from strongly to mildly alkaline. They have a pH of 9-12 and clean by converting fatty soil (grease) to soap, a process known as saponification. If chlorinated they can also break down proteins. Alkaline detergents are used to remove grease from ovens and stoves, for clearing blocked drains and at lower concentrations, in dish washing powders. The alkalis most commonly used are sodium hydroxide (in crystalline, solution or spray form), sodium metasilicate (crystals) and sodium carbonate (crystals and solution). All alkaline detergents must be handled with great care, particularly sodium hydroxide, and protective clothing should be worn. Manufacturers usually give advice on appropriate safety precautions on the product's container. Alkaline detergents cannot be used on aluminium and galvanised surfaces and strong alkalis can damage a range of materials including rubber, fabric, etc.

Sodium hydroxide is extremely caustic and corrosive (especially to aluminium) and should only be used where a very strong alkali is needed e.g. for oven cleaning.
Sodium metasilicate is less caustic and less corrosive and is the detergent most commonly used in dish washing formulations to emulsify grease. The alkaline silicates are better at penetrating soil and are easier to rinse off. Dishwashing detergents can remove the pattern from crockery not specifically designed for use in dishwashers.
Sodium carbonate is the least corrosive. It is cheap and although a relatively weak detergent is recommended for use in crystal form for unblocking drains or in combination with other detergents.

Trisodium phosphate is alkaline but relatively non caustic and is a good emulsifier with dispersive properties. For this reason it is often a component of cleaning agents.

Heavy duty alkaline cleaners work best for heavy deposits of organic soil and are particularly effective at removing burnt food deposits. More general purpose alkaline cleaners will remove moderate soil.

Acid Cleaners - Strong inorganic acids, pH 1-3, can remove dried on or encrusted soil and are widely used for the removal of limescale. Acids react with limescale and mineral deposits to give water-soluble salts. Acid cleaners should be handled with care and should not be allowed to come in contact with the skin. They must never be used in conjunction with toilet cleaners and disinfectants based on hypochlorite as they react to form the highly toxic gas chlorine. Some acid toilet cleaners are in powdered form and are based on acidic salts such as sodium bisulphate and sodium persulphate which release sulphuric acid on contact with water. Moderately strong acids, such as phosphoric and sulphamic, can be used to remove all but the most excessive limescale build up. Acid cleaners usually require a contact time of 2 to 3 hours to be effective. In combination with wetting agents they can be used in bottle washing.

Weaker organic acids, such as citric, gluconic acetic and tartaric acids, pH 3-5, are much safer to handle. A dilute solution of acetic acid can be used to clean plastic laminates, e.g. on table tops and work surfaces

4.1.6 Detergent Formulation

Cleaning products are formulated or built with fairly specific tasks in mind and are a careful blend of different chemicals each performing a specific function (see Table 4.1). The precise composition varies with task but for cost and environmental reasons it should not contain superfluous components. Components should be at an appropriate concentration for the conditions of use and type of soil.

Detergents in most common usage are still mainly liquid or powder (see also 4.2.5) and an initial decision in formulating a detergent is the type of main active cleaning agent it should contain (see 4.1) which in turn is related to use. For example a high foaming detergent is appropriate for hand-washing but not machine washing. A typical general purpose cleaner could have the following type of composition; alkaline builders to break up grease, a surfactant to improve wetting, dispersion and rinsability and sequesterants to stabilize inorganic salts (less important in soft water areas).

Table 4.2. Summary of the Properties of Various Types of Surfactant Detergents

ANIONIC		NON-IONIC	CATIONIC
Soap	Soapless		
hydrophobic tail / COO^- / hydrophilic head	hydrophobic tail / SO_3^{2-} SO_4^{2-} / hydrophilic head	hydrophobic tail / ether / OH / hydrophilic head	hydrophobic tail / $CH_3 - N^+ - CH_3$ / CH_3 / hydrophilic head
Negatively charged ion e.g. sodium stearate, potassium laurate	Negative charged ion e.g. alkylbenzene sulphate	Does not ionise e.g. alkylphenol ethoxylate	Positively charged ion e.g. cetyl trimethyl ammonium bromide (cetrimide)
Notes:- Forms scum in hard water Expensive	May cause skin problems e.g. contact dermatitis Cheap	Expensive	Inactivated by hard water Expensive Good antistatic agent Antibacterial properties

4.2 Disinfection

Disinfection, the reduction in microorganisms to an acceptable level, must not be confused with sterilisation. The latter refers to the complete removal of all microorganisms and spores. The term sterilant is a term sometimes incorrectly applied to disinfectants.

4.2.1 Disinfection by Cleaning

If correctly carried out, thorough cleaning may remove a high proportion of the microbial contamination from surfaces. However, much depends on the design, construction and condition of the surface being cleaned. Soft, porous, chipped and worn surfaces are far more difficult to clean. Cleaning materials, e.g. cloths, mops etc., must themselves be clean and cleaning solutions correctly made up. In key areas, such as food-preparation areas and washing/toilet facilities, disinfection by cleaning may not be adequate to reduce microorganisms to the low level necessary to prevent cross-contamination. In such cases additional heat or chemical disinfection is required as well.

4.2.2 Disinfection by Heat

Bacteria heated above their maximum temperature for growth for a sufficient period of time, will be destroyed and disinfection by heat is a reliable method for killing pathogenic organisms. Pathogens, apart from spore formers, are usually heat sensitive. The efficacy of disinfection by heat depends upon a variety of factors and it can be difficult to ensure that the entire surface to be disinfected is at the appropriate temperature. However, heat is a component of a number of disinfecting procedures including hot water rinses and the use of steam which possesses latent heat. Moist heat is more effective at killing than dry heat. High temperatures are costly to generate and for this reason, for large surface areas, heat is usually combined with the use of chemical disinfectants.

4.2.3 Chemical Disinfectants

In some cases it is impractical to disinfect by heat, and cleaning may need to be combined with the use of a chemical disinfectant. Care must be taken in the choice and use of disinfectants. No single disinfectant is universally ideal despite manufacturers' claims to the contrary! Some are not suitable for food-preparation areas, others are expensive, all may have their efficiency greatly reduced if used incorrectly. Factors influencing their use are summarised in Table 4.3

Key features of disinfectants which are used in food plants are that they must be non-toxic, non-tainting and effective. This reduces the range or types of chemicals that can be used.

Table 4.3 Factors Influencing the Use of Chemical Disinfectants

FACTOR	EFFECT
Temperature	Microorganisms are usually killed more effectively at elevated temperatures
Concentration	Usually, the more concentrated the disinfectant the quicker the kill. However, higher concentrations are usually more irritant or toxic and more corrosive to construction materials. Use at too low a concentration can increase the chances of resistance.
Contact Time	The destruction of microorganisms follows a logarithmic pattern, e.g. if 90% are killed after 10 min, 99% are killed after 20 mins and 99.9% after 30 mins. However, if the initial number of microorganisms was 1 million (10^6) and 99.9% are killed then this would leave 1,000 (10^3) microorganisms left, which may be more than enough to cause illness. The practical implications of this are twofold: 1. If larger numbers of microorganisms are present then a longer contact time is necessary 2. Disinfectants do not work instantly give them time.
Cleanliness	The efficacy of disinfectants is reduced in the presence of soil. Only use them on cleaned surfaces.
pH	Use at the correct pH: small changes can affect the activity of disinfectants.
Water Hardness	Hard water reduces the efficacy of disinfectants
Biofilms	Biofilms protect microorganisms from disinfectant activity. Prevent formation of biofilms by design if possible, or by effective cleaning.

N.B. Diluted disinfectant solutions must be disposed of immediately after use. Used solutions, especially those containing soil can act as good growth media, particularly for some types of bacteria, e.g *Pseudomonus spp.*

Disinfectants vary both in the way in which they affect microorganisms and in the type of microorganisms destroyed. Good disinfectants have a wide range (broad spectrum) of activity, killing many types of organisms. Others have a much more limited range and few have any significant effect on bacterial spores. Some disinfectants are bactericidal actually killing bacteria, others are bacteriostatic merely preventing the growth of bacteria (similarly 'mycocidal' and 'mycostatic' refer to fungi, 'viricidal' to viruses and 'sporicidal' to spores). Disinfectants do not work instantly. A minimum of two minutes contact time is necessary for a good disinfectant, with a susceptible microorganism, in ideal conditions. Other disinfectants may require much longer contact times.

Disinfectant solutions should be made up correctly, following the manufacturers instructions. Solutions that are too dilute will be ineffective, those that are too concentrated may be dangerous to use. Some disinfectant solutions deteriorate rapidly if left and therefore should be made up daily. Dirty diluted disinfectant solutions can actually contain large numbers of growing bacteria! Chemical disinfectants perform less well when diluted with hard rather than soft water, are more effective at high temperatures and are affected by pH changes. If the use of a disinfectant was identified as critical within the HACCP plan, then part of the HACCP plan would include checking that the disinfectant had been made up and used correctly. Whatever the type of disinfectant, these checks need to be rapid and able to give 'real time' results e.g. by chemical titration or using analytical test strips. General information on the efficacy of the disinfectant will have to be provided by suppliers as part of their compliance with the Biocidal Products Directive (Appendix 7).

4.2.4 Types of Liquid Disinfectant
A range of disinfectants is available, the most common ones being based on the following chemicals:

Hypochlorites / Chlorine Based - These include hypochlorites, liquid chlorine, chlorine dioxide as well as organic chloramines. They owe their anti-microbial action to the release of free chlorine in solution. As a group they have many advantages in the food industry. They are relatively inexpensive and have a wide range of antimicrobial activity (including viricidal and limited sporicidal activitiy).In working concentrations, used on food preparation surfaces, they have relatively little taste or smell. Hypochlorite solutions may deteriorate on storage and can have a corrosive effect on some surfaces. Their biggest disadvantage is that they are more readily inactivated by organic debris than most other disinfectants. Hypochlorite solutions are often purchased at concentrations of about 100,000 ppm (parts per million) i.e.10% of available chlorine, although some cheaper brands may only be half as strong. For disinfecting clean work surfaces, this will need dilution to between 100 and 200 ppm. More heavily soiled surfaces require solutions of about 1000 ppm or even stronger for some hospital use where the presence of particularly harmful pathogens in the presence of organic matter is suspected. In such instances the destruction of the pathogen and the prevention of cross infection is the main priority in advance of cleaning. Hypochlorites are anionic and must NOT be mixed with cationic detergents (see 4.1.4). Nor should hypochlorites be mixed with acid cleaners since chlorine is produced, inhalation of which can lead to irritation and damage of the lining of the respiratory tract. Hypochlorites should not be used on fabrics as they remove colour. Thickening agents are added to some products to make them cling to surfaces (e.g. toilet bowls to increase contact time). Organic-based chlorine sanitisers which can be added to water to clean fruits and vegetables include sodium or potassium isocyanuric acid derivatives.

Quaternary Ammonium Compounds (QAC or Quats) - These are cationic surfactants which vary depending upon the level and type of substitution of hydrogen ions within an ammonium (NH_4^+) group. Some possess antibacterial properties being used for disinfection, and are more effective in alkaline conditions. Generally, they have a more limited range of activity than hypochlorites being more effective against Gram positive than Gram negative bacteria. Some are to be bacteristatic whilst others bactericidal. Quats are more expensive than hypochlorites and some are relatively easily inactivated by organic soil (but less so than hypochlorites) and anionic detergents. They can be used on most work surfaces or for rinsing equipment as they are non-corrosive, virtually odourless and tasteless and can penetrate porous surfaces. Quats tend to leave a residual bacteriostatic film on surfaces.

Iodophors - These are soluble iodine complexes incorporating a non-ionic detergent and phosphoric acid buffer to maintain a pH of 3 - 5 where they are most active. They have bactericdal action with a wide range of activity, are non-corrosive, non-irritating, non-toxic and less affected by organic soil but are expensive. They are used widely in some types of food premises, e.g. breweries and dairies.

Biguanides - These are effective against bacteria, yeasts and moulds (not spores or viruses). They are similar to quats in that they are cationic bactericides. They do not have good wetting properties, are non-foaming, non-tainting and are easily rinsed. They are insoluble above pH10 and should not be used with caustic detergents. They can be used to disinfect equipment in soak baths.

Amphoteric Surfactants - These vary in chemical composition and not all exhibit antimicrobial activity. Those that do are effective in acid solutions, have low toxicity, and are relatively non-corrosive and odourless. They foam easily and are not suitable for use in CIP systems or in pressure sprays. They are used in skin / hand formulations and for soaking equipment.

Acidic Compounds - A range of organic acids including acetic, lactic, propionic and peracetic acids can be used for terminal disinfection. These active compounds are based upon organic acids or mineral acids combined with an anionic surfactant. They neutralise alkaline residues as well as disinfecting and work well on stainless steel surfaces. Some non-foaming formulations are finding use in CIP systems and peracetic acid is used in dairies, breweries and soft drinks plants and is effective against *Salmonella* and *Listeria*.

Alcohols - Two of the most commonly used alcohols are ethanol and isopropanol. These can be used in hand disinfectants or in "dry cleaning" (see 3.4). They are suitable for lightly soiled surfaces and have the advantage that they evaporate rapidly leaving a dry surface.

Phenolic Disinfectants - A number of different types of phenolic disinfectants are available, all of which are anionic including :-

(a) White fluid phenolics

(b) Clear soluble phenolics

(c) Chlorinated phenols

(d) Complex phenols

As a rule (a) and (b) are good disinfectants, possessing a broad spectrum of activity but can be toxic to unprotected skin.   Unlike hypochlorites, phenolics are not so readily activated by organic debris. Their **strong smell and residual after-taste** on work surfaces limit their use to drains, floors and toilets. Because of their powerful tainting potential and the transfer of phenolic taste e.g. via, clothes, blades, to food or food surfaces many food companies will not use them at all, but they may find use in catering operations. Chlorination of phenols reduces their range of antimicrobial activity, makes them more susceptible to organic debris but does allow them to be used on the skin (see table 4.4).

Pine Fluids - Disinfectants based on pine fluids often have poor antimicrobial activity but their pine smell makes them a more popular household disinfectant, although they may also be used in some small catering premises. Pine fluids may be blended with phenolic disinfectants to give better antimicrobial activity. Their use is not generally recommended in food premises partly because of their tainting potential and relatively poor antimicrobial activity.

Tables 4.5 and 4.6 compare the more common disinfectants used in the food industry.

Table 4.4 Typical Formulations or Combinations Used in Sanitisers

FOOD SURFACES	
DETERGENT	**DISINFECTANT**
Anionic surfactants (less than 5%)	Sodium hypochlorite
Non-ionic surfactants	QUATS or Iodophors
Inorganic alkali	Hypochlorites or QUATS
Inorganic acid	Cationic surfactants or iodophors
SKIN (anti-bacterial hand soap)	
Non-ionic surfactants less than 5% Anionic surfactants less than 5%	Chlorophenols (less than 5%)

Table 4.5 Site and Mechanisms of Activity of Various Disinfectants (depending on concentration)

Steam	Ozone	Chlorine	Iodophor	Quats
Moist-coagulation and denaturation of cell proteins Dry-oxidation and dehydration	Oxidising agent. Production of free radicals damages cell, especially cell membranes	Oxidising agent. Attacks cell membrane and cytoplasmic enzymes and other proteins	Oxidising agent. Attacks cytoplasmic enzymes and other proteins	Non oxidising agents. Attacks cell membrane and cytoplasmic proteins. Causes coagulation of cell protein and cell leakage

Table 4.6 Comparison of Various Disinfectants Available for Use on Food Contact Surfaces

CHARACTERISTIC	STEAM	OZONE	CHLORINE	IODOPHORS	QUATS	ACIDIC COMPDS.
Effectiveness Gram +ve	Good	Good	Good	Good	Good	Good
Gram -ve	Good	Good	Good	Good	Poor	Good
Spores	Good	Some	Good	Some	Some	Some
Effect of Hard Water	NA	NA	No	Slightly	Some	Slightly
Effect of organic matter / residual soil	No	Yes	Yes (high)	Yes (moderate)	Yes (low)	Yes (low)
Active residue	No	No	No	Yes	Yes	Yes
Corrosiveness	No	No (except natural rubber)	Yes	Slightly	No	Slightly
Adverse effect on Skin	Yes	Yes at levels above 0.2ppm	Yes	Yes	No	Yes
Stability of use	No Condenses	No Decomposes To oxygen	No Dissipates rapidly	Yes	Yes	Yes
Penetration	Poor	Poor	Poor	Good	Good	Good
Stability in hard water	NA	NA	Unstable	Unstable	Stable	Stable
Cost	High	Very low	Low	Medium	Medium	Medium

NA = Not Applicable

4.2.5 Fogging, Foams, Gels and Powders

In addition to the traditional forms of liquid detergents and disinfectants alternatives such as fogs or mists, foam and gels can be used. Foams are more viscous than mists and are used to remove more firmly adhering soil when cleaning large, complex or inaccessible surfaces. Unlike ordinary liquids, foams cling to surfaces for longer and then collapse and release fresh chemicals ensuring maximum contact time with the soil. Conventional foam detergents can suffer from poor adhesion to vertical surfaces, especially if dirty, resulting in reduced contact times. Specialised long cling foams combat this and there are claims that they are more efficient in their application, as they are used at lower concentrations and in smaller volumes. They can be applied quickly but need to be left for at least 20 minutes depending on formulation and soiling (see Fig 1.1). Being more visible foams can be applied more evenly, although they can sometimes be difficult to rinse off completely. Anti-bacterial agents (e.g. QUATS) are sometimes included in the rinse solution. One of the problems with fogs and foam is that they can leave mineral and other deposits on surfaces especially in hard water areas. Products containing chelating or sequestering agents can help to prevent this.

Thixotropic gels (fluid when stirred reverting to a gel on standing) have an even greater contact time than foams and greater rinsability although tend to be more expensive. A variety of powder detergents can be used in dishwashers or to clean heavily grease encrusted equipment, e.g. deep fat fryers. These can sometimes be slow to dissolve in water and may require special health and safety precautions such as masks and gloves.

Disinfectant fogging can be used to reduce the microbial count of air as well as surfaces e.g. in chillers, store areas, etc. Fogging uses a spray mist of disinfectant and can only be performed outside production hours because of the health risk to workers and the possibility of product contamination. The mists are generated at low pressure but only affect smooth horizontal surfaces and will leave residual deposits of disinfectants. Fogging is ineffective for the disinfection of vertical surfaces, the undersides of equipment or dismantled equipment. Fogging is best regarded as an additional safeguard rather than a replacement to disinfection routines. Under typical conditions fogging requires a minimum of 30 minutes to enable the fog to disperse and destroy any microorganisms. An additional period of about 1hr is then required to allow any droplets time to settle out from the atmosphere. Fogging usually requires some means of mechanical dispersion, e.g. by compressed air driven fogging nozzles which can be permanently plumbed in or portable. Fogs or mists can also be used in cleaning but only for lightly soiled surfaces. Residual detergent and loosened soil are then removed by rinsing.

4.2.6 Comparison of Foam and Gel Cleaning

Many companies are moving from traditional bucket and brush approach to cleaning to one which makes use of foam and gels. The reason cited for this change included less available time for cleaning, fewer staff, interruption of production, excessive water usage leading to microbial problems, the need for safe chemicals and practices, the need for environmentally acceptable chemicals and the fact that biocidal products will have to be registered in the future. Points were raised concerning both foam and gel cleaning in comparison to traditional methods which are summarised as follows:

Foam Cleaning	Gel Cleaning
• less labour intensive than traditional methods	• less labour intensive than traditional methods
• foam is visible	• reasonably visible/may be coloured
• requirement for foam stability	• gels on dilution
• better control of chemicals	• better control of chemicals
• foam does not stick to vertical surfaces	• gel sticks to vertical surfaces
• high water usage for rinsing	• easy rinse, less water usage
• reasonable efficiency	• very effective even on tenacious soils

However, use of this new approach needs to be validated and monitored to ensure an adequate reduction in microorganisms is achieved and that appropriate levels of surface cleanliness are achieved. This emphasises the scientific approach to cleaning, it must be efficient, quick and cost effective and there must be a planned approach. Low pressure systems are preferred, and better dosing and hygiene monitoring systems are desirable (Rigarlsford 1999).

4.2.7 Thin Film Cleaning

One recent development has been thin film cleaning (Henkel-Ecolab GMBH & Co.). This cleans by intensive soaking with a thin film applied using specialised equipment with the film sticking to the surface. Wetting agents are included to promote soil penetration. There is mechanical cleaning action as the slowly collapsing film cuts through the soil. Application of the film is possible without an intensive pre-rinse, even on very soiled surfaces, the film and soil are easily rinsed and remain wet and visible throughout cleaning. The advantages cited by the company are reduction in labour costs, improved contact due to the sticking properties of the foam, a reduction in pre- and post-application rinsing time plus water, waste water and energy saving.

4.2.8 Assessing Disinfectant Efficacy
In selling a disinfectant, sales staff will try to convince you of their product's efficacy in killing microorganisms and may quote numerical values for particular tests.

Rideal Walker Test One of the oldest tests it compares the killing efficiency of the product to that of phenol using a standard culture of a test organism (*Salmonella typhi* or *Staphyloccocus aureus*).

Chick-Martin test This has similarities to the Rideal Walker test but a sterilised yeast suspension is added to "mimic" organic debris that may be present on a surface.

Kelsey Sykes Test Disinfectant solutions are prepared in hard water and the test can be performed with or without organic soil. A standard suspension of a test organism is added to dilutions of disinfectant. Samples are then taken at regular intervals and transferred to a liquid recovery medium. These are examined for growth 48 hours later.

European Suspension Test This uses 5 test organisms. Bovine Serum Albumen (BSA) is used to mimic organic soil. A standard microbial inoculum is added to the lowest concentration recommended for use by the manufacturers. Samples are withdrawn and after neutralising the disinfectant viable counts are performed.   For the disinfectant to be acceptable the lowest concentration of disinfectant must achieve a 5 log kill.

4.2.9 Ozone as a Terminal Disinfectant
Although its disinfectant properties have been known about for over 50 years there has recently been renewed interest in the use of ozone gas as an alternative to chemical disinfection.

The ozone (O_3) molecule (see Fig 4.3) is a powerful oxidant which chemically reacts with microbial cells resulting in cell damage and death.   The mechanism of ozone toxicity is not fully known although evidence suggests that free radicals (hydroxyl $OH^\bullet$; superoxide $O_2^{\bullet-}$) as well as hydrogen peroxide (H_2O_2) are products of ozone decomposition which can exert a cytotoxic action.   In comparison ozone is one of the most powerful oxidising agents and has a 52% more oxidising power than chlorine, an additional advantage is that it rapidly decomposes to form oxygen. The advantages and disadvantages of ozone as a terminal disinfectant are summarised in table 4.7.

In order to ensure the that residual microorganisms are exposed to sufficient ozone the following need to be considered:

- Volume to be treated
- Level and type of microbial contamination
- Absorbency of materials
- Nature of materials
- Humidity levels
- Temperature
- Air turnover/exchange
- Time available window of opportunity

Fig. 4.3 A diagram of an Ozone Molecule (O_3)

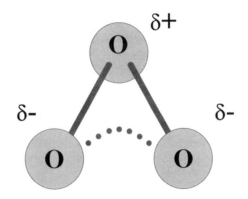

4.2.10 Summary of Rules for Disinfection

1. Is cleaning alone sufficient or is there a need for extra disinfection?

2. Choose heat for disinfection where possible.

3. If a chemical disinfectant is to be used, clean surfaces first. Is ozone appropriate? Choose a reputable liquid brand with little or no residual taste or smell.

4. Make up disinfectant solutions daily in clean containers, following the manufacturer's instructions and using soft water. Equipment for applying disinfectants should itself be clean.

5. Apply disinfectant solutions liberally.

6. Allow sufficient time for the disinfectant to work. Rinse.

7. Discard any left-over disinfectant.

Table 4.7 The Advantages and Disadvantages of Ozone as a Terminal Disinfectant

Advantages
Powerful oxidising agent
Kills broad spectrum of microorganisms
Kills insect pests at higher concentrations
Effective at low concentrations
Effective in wet and dry environments
Effective on horizontal and vertical surfaces
Effective on airborne organisms
Recognised as GRAS under FDA rules *
Reverts to molecular oxygen leaving no by products, toxic residues or residual contamination
Leaves no residual odour
Deodorises (destroys objectionable smells)
Is pH neutral (no change to acid / alkali balance)
Cheap and simple to produce
Minimal maintenance
Can be combined with other methods e.g. UV
Disadvantages
Can attack natural rubber
Health and Safety restrictions if above 0.2 ppm for more than 15 minutes
Poor penetrating ability

* GRAS - generally regarded as safe

* FDA - Food and Drug Administration U.S.A

4.3 Sanitisers

These are essentially detergent / disinfectants (see Table 4.4) and are used to reduce the number of stages in a cleaning programme. In addition they are likely to contain sequestering agents, buffers and even preservatives in some cases.

In general terms, using a sanitiser is usually more expensive and less effective but quicker than using separate chemicals in successive stages. For this reason they are best used in areas of light soiling or in hand-wash preparations.

4.4 Resistance to Biocides

The term biocide (literally life killing) within the cleaning context includes disinfectants and sanitisers. It could under other circumstances include antiseptics, antibiotics and even preservatives. As previously discussed each biocide has a "spectrum of activity" i.e. a range of organisms against which it is effective. The reverse of this is that different microorganisms can display, to a greater or lesser extent, resistance to disinfectants. This phenomenon is more readily recognised with antibiotics and the problems posed by multiple antibiotic resistant pathogens.

Resistance to disinfectants is less likely than antibiotics which are usually more specific in action where resistance is more likely to arise by means of mutation. Table 4.4 illustrates that most disinfectants do not show selective toxicity and will affect multiple bacterial structures or functions. However increased resistance to disinfectants can occur and is more likely to happen if disinfectants are used when too dilute or when used for inadequate times. Both will tend to "select out" the more resistant organisms from the microbial population within the food premises. Additionally some resistance to disinfectants, which can be genetically transmitted, has been reported. This is less likely to occur with hypochlorite based disinfectants and more likely with the Quats. In the latter case plasmids, that code for proteins capable of pumping the Quats out of the cell before they can cause damage, have been found. Resistance can also occur if the bacterium can prevent the disinfectant from entering the cell. Resistance to biocides by viruses is due to other mechanisms.

Because of possible disinfectant resistance it can be wise to mimic policies in hospitals where antibiotic use is rotated. This would necessitate rotating disinfectants used within cleaning programmes e.g. hypochlorite disinfectant would be substituted with a Quat for a short period of time, thus helping to eliminate the build up of resistant populations. However, in each case the use of the disinfectant needs to be validated (see 6.7).

4.5 Legislation and Safe Handling of Cleaning Equipment

4.5.1 Biocidal Products Directive

Biocides (disinfectants) are an important part of cleaning especially in the production of high risk foods. It is important for anyone using a biocide to have confidence in its efficacy and safety. Evidence is needed to demonstrate efficacy in order to support a due diligence defence. For this and other reasons cleaning programmes should be validated (see 5.5 and 6.7) however this can be difficult for many smaller food producers such as caterers.

Currently, the testing of disinfectants is compulsory in some EU countries, e.g. Germany, France, Holland although not in the UK. However, from about May 2000 the Biocidal Products Directive will be introduced. This will require that only biocides listed and authorised in accordance with the Directive can be used. The biocide's efficacy will have to be tested against a range of target organisms under standard conditions, by an independent authorised body. Primary manufacturers will have to bear the cost of testing but it should allow users to be better informed about the products they are buying and using. It should also allow easier comparison between products.

An additional requirement under the Directive is that a full toxicological evaluation of the biocide is carried out. This should include the impact of the biocide on the environment and on humans as well as the physical and chemical properties and the effect of contact with food. Of increasing concern is the biodegradability of the chemicals used in cleaning.

The effect of the Directive could be a more restricted range of biocides and increased costs although this may be minimised by the removal of trade barriers and greater competition. Nevertheless the overall result will be better information for users in making risk assessments and greater use of more effective biocides.

In addition to biocides used as disinfectants in cleaning programmes, the directive also covers chemicals used in pest control, and as preservatives (excluding those covered in food standards directives).

4.5.2 Safe Handling of Cleaning Materials

Cleaning can be a dangerous operation as equipment may need dismantling which can expose blades. Water used in cleaning can give rise to slippery floors.
Detergents and disinfectants can be irritant and toxic and are potentially hazardous to

both operatives or people in the vicinity of cleaning. For this reason cleaning is covered by the 1974 Health and Safety at Work Act. More specific legislation under this Act concerns the Control of Substances Hazardous to Health Regulations 1994 more usually referred to as COSHH. These regulations require (like HACCP) the hazards to be identified followed by a risk assessment and the implementation of appropriate measures to control the hazards.

Risk assessments start with an examination of the place to be cleaned and the materials used followed by an identification of all the possible hazards. Hazard identification can be based upon experience or by the application of cause and effect analysis (Appendix 2). This is followed by an identification of employees who might be exposed to the hazard and an evaluation of risk. Risk includes the probability of the event occurring combined with the severity or consequences arising from the hazard. Control measures need to be designed and implemented for those hazards likely to occur or are remote but have a high severity. A risk assessment matrix can be used to help prioritise action. The risk assessment process should be well documented and reviewed regularly to ensure it is still appropriate. Any changes to the cleaning methods or materials should be followed by a COSHH assessment update.

The Personal Protective Equipment (PPE) at Work Regulations 1992 require the employer to provide relevant employees with suitable protective clothing. This includes hand, eye and respiratory protection as well as protective overalls. Employees must be appropriately trained and informed concerning use of the equipment and information on first aid provided.

4.5.3 Labelling and Storage of Cleaning Materials

Labelling of Cleaning Materials
All potentially hazardous chemicals must be labelled and accompanied by a hazard symbol indicating the type of consequences / danger. Suppliers should also provide a safety data sheet containing full details of the product and its hazardous classification under the Chemicals (Hazard, Information and Packaging) Regulations 1993.

Storage of Cleaning Materials
The following set of simple rules should be followed:-
1.   Store cleaning materials in a separate, identified, locked room with restricted access which should be:-

      (a) dry and cool;

(b) adequately sized and ventilated

(c) well lit and kept clean

2. Acid and alkaline products should be stored apart

3. Store acid materials separately from chlorine-based products

4. Store chlorine-based products in dark conditions

5. Clearly label ALL containers

6. Do not transfer cleaning products to alternative containers for storage. The product may react with the material of the new container. Use before expiry date.

7. Take care in cleaning out containers, e.g. vessels containing sugar cleaned with sodium hydroxide, produce carbon monoxide gas.

8. Container lids should be tightly fitted and/or firmly screwed on. All deliveries should be checked for damage.

9. There should be adequate washing facilities for ordinary and emergency use. Appropriate protective clothing gloves, goggles, aprons, masks and boots should be worn.

10. Automatic dispensers should be used if possible. Appropriate sinks and work surfaces should be available for dispensing / diluting from strong solutions.

11. Accidental spillage should be dealt with immediately and procedures for dealing with injuries / or spillages must be fully documented.

4.6 Selection and Purchasing of Cleaning /Disinfectant materials

Maintenance of good hygiene in food preparation premises, whether in the catering or manufacturing industry, usually involves chemical products. The preceding chapters provide background information on what type to select, how to use them, when to use them, under what conditions and how to manage their use.

4.6.1 Dependence on Production Process

For many production process, however, the nature of the food and the method of processing influences both the type of soil and the disinfection requirements. Some processes, such as cooking in a steam-jacketed kettle may, if the stirring is not totally effective, produce charred soil residues. Some processes may produce a high protein or high lipid residue. The effectiveness of a given cleaning agent will be determined by the nature of this soil. Cleaning chemicals can be selected on the basis of claims made by the supplier but will, nevertheless, need to be assessed in use on the actual soil on or in the user's processing equipment. Similarly, selection of a disinfectant or whether to employ a sanitiser may be based on the supplier's claims. Chapter 6 describes the basis of evaluating performance.

Once selected, it is important for the user to be confident that the supplier will not deliberately downgrade performance by reduction of the level of any active component in an attempt to increase profits. Independent testing can provide assurance without the user carrying out regular cleaning performance trials or else using laboratory testing to check composition?

4.6.2 The RIPHH's Hygiene Product Certification Service

The Royal Institute of Public Health and Hygiene (RIPHH), a UK based organisation, with the aims and objectives of improving public health in the UK and elsewhere, developed a hygiene product certification service in 1904 to evaluate, on an annual basis, the hygienic merit of products that made a contribution to health and hygiene. This service has been in existence ever since, although the types of product it evaluates have undergone many changes during this period. The majority of products are now chemical and include cleaning, disinfectants and skin care materials. Products are now received for testing from many overseas countries.

All products are tested initially on submission by a supplier and then annually to check that they are of the same quality as they were when initially submitted. Many products have been tested annually for decades and one for in excess of 60 years. If the test results are satisfactory, the supplier is awarded a certificate which has a duration of one year. Product formulations may change but this must not be accompanied by a drop in performance. Typical changes that suppliers make to their products include performance improvements, increased bio-degradability and modifications forced by raw material supply variations. As new products are submitted for testing and certification, new types of active component are appearing. Recently, a new cationic surfactant became available which may be used with anionic surfactants without compromising its antibacterial activity (the majority, however, cannot be mixed without loss of performance see 4.1.4). These changes reflect a dynamic industry.

The wide range of tests required to check the ongoing formulation reflects the number of active components available to the product formulators. Examples of those used in cleaning products include: surfactants (non-ionic, cationic, anionic, amphoteric), fatty acids and their salts, solvents (water miscible and immiscible), acids (hydrochloric, phosphoric, sulphamic and citric), alkalis (hydroxides, silicates, carbonates), sequestrants (EDTA, NTA, polyphosphates). Disinfectant components include: acids (inorganic and organic), alkalis, lower alcohols, biguanidines, bronopol, chlorine release products, glycols, quaternary ammonium, peroxygen compounds. Additional tests are employed to substantiate those for individual components. Wherever possible, official, standard methods of test are used.

In addition to the laboratory tests, all literature is checked to ensure that there are no errors. Labels and safety data sheets must contain the appropriate health and safety information. Labels and instructions for use must be clear as these may also influence the test programme. Advertising and promotional literature must be accurate. The service does not include any evaluation of costs so does not comment on 'value for money'. This is for the user to check when selecting a product and programme for cleaning.

To help users select products that are routinely tested and certificated by the RIPHH, a Register of Certificated Products is published (free of charge to users). Products and their suppliers (and details) are listed, along with information designed to assist in selection such as the use, type and form. Product labels may have wording indicating that they hold a certificate and may also bear the RIPPH's logo.

Chapter 5 - ORGANISING AND MANAGING CLEANING
- Planning to Succeed
5.1 Why plan

The cleaning plan for the company may take a number of forms varying from a simple schedule detailing frequency to a complete manual containing individual cleaning procedures for key items of equipment or food contact surfaces. In any of these forms it provides direction to the operator and feedback for the manager- the value and benefits of the direction it provides and of the feedback it produces is related to the quality of the plan.

Fig. 5.1 Aim before you Fire!

Management may organise their cleaning activities into defined cleaning approaches ranging from cleaning out of place (COP), cleaning in place (CIP) or standard cleaning of an environment . Cleaning of an area may involve combinations of these three approaches.

The management process of organising and planning a cleaning system will be discussed including the criteria for selection of chemicals . The remainder of the chapter will then review COP and CIP cleaning approaches. Chapter 7 discusses the building of a cleaning plan and includes more detailed examples of the standard cleaning approach. Chapter 6 provides a detailed analysis of assessment approaches.

The information within the plan is dependent upon the needs of the business and the team and must contain sufficient detail to ensure that cleaning is effectively implemented and managed. The plan may assist the business to do the following:

- Provide clear instructions for the cleaning crew or operative
- Act as a training resource for new team members or as reference material for team
- Enable performance to be measured against agreed targets set within the plan
- Demonstrate compliance with law or market needs

The plan therefore allows clear communication within the cleaning team, and provides feedback to management. Performance can only be measured through a well designed plan and will provide management with factual information for achieving optimal control We will discuss the approaches to documenting the plan in section 5.6.

5.2 Planning for Profit Through Control

Fig. 5.2 Pie chart showing resource use in cleaning

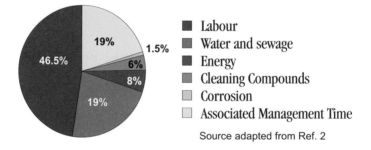

Source adapted from Ref. 2

A major goal of any business is to minimise costs and to maximise profit and the management team must therefore ensure that the business is run efficiently and effectively. Management optimise the limited food control resources to achieve agreed standards and build monitoring tools to check the cleaning plan is working. The approach adopted by management in the planning process can determine the degree of success.

Effective cleaning demands that a plan is consistently followed and resources are well used. Senior management must find cleaning sufficiently important to produce a plan with suitable   budgets and targets which the business must follow. An economic argument is normally the best approach to persuade the owners or senior management of the benefits of optimal cleaning. The allocation of specific responsibility for ensuring a cost effective clean and the effort demonstrated by the planning process will ensure a much higher degree of commitment throughout the business. Regular reporting on the performance of the plan and communication of results to the workforce and senior management ensures both performance and resources are used correctly. Chapter 7 describes the management tools which can support effective cost control.

5.3 Management Awareness and Understanding

A plan is needed that will meet the specific cleaning objectives of the company and that fits into its existing management approach. The planner needs to consider the current and future legislation regarding hygiene and food safety and the increasing environmental pressure to manage resources including water and control of the effluent. Emerging pathogens, problems with biofilms and knowledge of alternative chemical cleaning approaches and disinfecting agents, such as ozone, all require the business to review their plans and update where necessary. Labour costs typically account for 60 - 80% of the total cleaning cost. This means that the human resource should be effectively trained, managed and utilised.

5.3.1 Opportunities to Reduce Effluent in the Cleaning Approach

The detailed knowledge gained through preparing thorough cleaning plans enables opportunities for better control to be identified and analysed objectively. Legal pressures and environmental groups push the business to reduce the quantity and toxicity of their effluent. This has forced many companies to review their existing approaches to cleaning as this may generate waste or collect product which can be recycled.

The options to tanker waste solids off site are being reduced through increased cost and the tougher legal requirements of traceability for certain types of waste (e.g waste meat cannot be used for landfill as cattle cannot graze on this soil following the BSE legislation). This tougher environmental legislation and the Biocides Directive will mean closer scrutiny of the amount and type of chemical cleaning products that are utilised throughout the factory. Companies are therefore re-appraising their cleaning programmes and using this as a means to examine the existing cleaning approaches and processing options to reduce the amount of water used and waste generated. When properly managed much of the "waste" may be re-worked or used in added value products. Replacement of water in cleaning by dry cleaning e.g. vacuuming or as a means of moving product by belts will be increasingly attractive to food companies.

5.4 Management Control

An effective monitoring system for all aspects of cleaning should be established, managed and used. Monitoring methods may consist of QC checks, pre start up checks (which may just be a visual inspection by a supervisor before production commences) and periodical audits. In order for the system to work effectively, these checks must be recorded and monitored. Documented procedures should be designed to effectively monitor the system and corrective actions and preventive measures need to be defined.

First level corrective action could be seen as "Fix it" i.e. when a failure is detected by monitoring the system, corrective action should ensure the immediate problem is resolved and the system is back in compliance. The second level corrective action could be seen as "Stop It" i.e. identify where and why a failure has occurred and take steps to prevent this recurring. (See Fig 6.5 to 6.8).

 The decision as to whether a system is in compliance is reached by analysis against the reference standard using agreed methods. Section 5.4.1 will discuss the standard whereas Chapter 6 will review the methods which may be used to check for compliance Further detail of IT software support systems which are specifically built to aid management control of cleaning programmes are discussed in Chapter 8.

5.4.1 Defining the Standard
The planning process demands that the management define the cleaning standard to be achieved in a given area and for specific contact surfaces. Previously suggested microbial and ATP targets for surfaces after cleaning are provided in Table 6.5 . Alternatively management may define the standard as "physically" clean in low risk areas were no visible sign of dirt is regarded as an adequate standard . Many small businesses will use "physically" clean - i.e no visibly remaining debris - see 6.2 for a description of methods to evaluate cleanliness.

This standard has severe limitations and management must be convinced this provides sufficient control of cleanliness. Many small businesses assume that if the chemicals they have purchased are working then achieving a "physically " clean surface or area is sufficient as the terminal sanitiser or disinfectant they use will adequately reduce microbial load.

5.5 Check Your Plan Works - Validating Cleaning Programmes
An alternative approach is for the business to "validate" the effectiveness of the existing cleaning programme and use the "physically" clean sensory and visual assessment methods to ensure compliance with the cleaning methods. Section 6.7 provides an example of an approach to validation. Table 5.1 describes a four level process which management may employ to validate the cleaning programmes or selected methods for critical control points.

Table 5.1 Approaches to Validating Cleaning Programmes

Level	Validation Approach	Description
1	Industrial	Accepted practice in the sector. Data from suppliers of cleaning materials based on trials held on similar surfaces and soil.
2	Theoretical	The method i.e. detergent, sanitiser and disinfectant has been shown to control the target organisms or remove known soil effectively
3	Modelling	Theoretical models may be used to indicate which organisms cannot survive or will be controlled by the cleaning programme- e.g. time, temperature or specific chemical
4	Trials	Specific factory trials (see section 6.7). These trials need to be well designed and scientifically justified

The business may use any combination of the above approaches to ensure that their cleaning programme is valid. Once the validity of a cleaning process is known then confirmation of control may be by visual inspection and may be further supported by microbiological or rapid surface testing at an agreed frequency. Small low risk businesses have traditionally relied on level 1 approach. Increasingly any high risk premises will need to employ higher level validation approaches to ensure effective control and support the defence of due diligence but this must not be recorded as the prime objective.

5.6 Types of plan - Documenting Your System

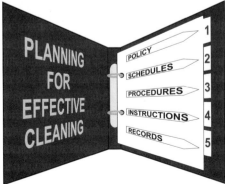

Fig. 5.3 Differing Shapes the Plan May Take

Fig. 5.4 Master Documents Contained Within the Cleaning Plan Manual

This system of formal documents defines responsibility, details authority and the roles and resources which are required to ensure correct operation. The five levels of documentation described in Figs 5.3 & 5.4 gradually become more specific to an activity. The documents are normally contained within a specific cleaning manual which contains an index of the procedures, work instructions, records and the schedule which details when the cleaning will occur. The detailed procedures may be on A4 format which can be laminated for use within the processing area. Alternatively they may be produced in the form of cleaning cards supported by diagrams and images which give clear instructions . The cards can be removed by the crew when a particular area or item is being cleaned.

The cleaning manual can be maintained using the normal document control system within the business to allow revision and replacement of outdated procedures or work instructions. Additionally the manual may contain a specific company cleaning or hygiene policy which can be supported by the objectives set for the operation in each area as detailed by the cleaning plan.

At the next level of documentation there are detailed procedures reflecting the principles and practices from the cleaning manual. These procedures will define responsibility and give outline instructions for activities.

Specific work instructions provide the detailed requirements for particular operations which support cleaning e.g. dismantling a cutting machine, removing light covers or cleaning out insectocutors. The final level of documentation will be the records of outputs from schedules, procedures and or work instructions.

5.6.1 Responsibility

Roles and authority should be defined within the cleaning plan and resources controlled and managed through the budgetary process and routine variance analysis . This involves defining roles and job descriptions in relation to the company structure. The cleaning approaches described are typically used by organisations who already use formal quality assurance systems and cleaning control is an extension of their existing system. Contract cleaning companies or chemical suppliers will also assist in documenting a system . Many variations will exist to the documentation - from a trained workforce and total absence of documentation to fully documented cleaning manual. Alternatively many small businesses - particularly in the catering sector, incorporate sufficient detail within the schedule to prevent the need for a full manual.

Therefore whether for equipment or premises, cleaning must be planned for it to be economical and effective. Cleaning must be consistently performed and this requires clear written instructions to ensure no matter who performs the cleaning it will be safely carried out and be effective. This written documentation, which could be required for a due diligence defence, is sometimes known as a cleaning schedule. Cleaning schedules have been described and should be adhered to, not produced only when audited and inspected, and cleaning operatives should be consulted in their construction. People who regularly clean areas and equipment often know the difficulties that may be encountered and involving them at the outset helps to instil ownership. Similarly cleaning should be considered, if possible, in the design and construction of plant or equipment. Individual cleaning schedules can be kept together to form a cleaning manual.

This is normally only possible when the range of chemicals being used is small and the cleaning procedures similar within the area. Additionally the instructions for dismantling and cleaning are often omitted if the production crew are responsible for cleaning their own equipment.

5.7 Cleaning Schedules - Factors to be Considered

Factors to be considered in the design of a cleaning schedule are summarised in Table 5.2.

Table 5.2 Factors to be Considered in the Design of a Cleaning Schedule

FACTORS	Management must consider:-
Plant Description or Location	intended product, whether high or low risk, size, temperature, humidity of area, surface finishes
Materials of Construction	can affect level of water pressure, and detergent or disinfectant used.
Availability of (including waste disposal)	electricity, steam etc., can dictate use of mobile or fixed Utilities equipment
Time Available (including shift patterns)	can dictate method of cleaning and choice of disinfectant e.g. use of ozone.
Operative Working Conditions	need for protective equipment, Health and Safety
Whether Disinfection Required or Not	related to risk and any HACCP plans.
Need For / Process of Validation	proving the cleaning is effective
Need for Monitoring	If CCP or not, choice of method.

5.7.1 Documentation

The cleaning plan or schedule itself should clearly identify why, who, how and when cleaning is to be performed. Staff doing the cleaning should be suitably trained and be aware of the standards required. The cleaning plan is often best accompanied by diagrams and pictures, and should take into consideration or include the following:

1. Clear definition of area or equipment to be cleaned.

2. For equipment, information on constructional materials and how the equipment should be dismantled needs to be provided. Many equipment manufacturers

provide cleaning schedules, advice on how this can be achieved plus guidance on safety and prevention of damage.

3. Type of soil to be expected with any hazards (chemical / microbiological) warnings.

4. Precise details on how cleaning is to be carried out - step by step account in order of what is to be done and how it is to be done. What chemicals to use, how to make them up, what to do with them afterwards, how long they are to be applied for, temperature, pressure. Details of any equipment to be used and how it is to be cared for.

5. Identification of problem areas or where extra care needed.

6. Time and people required

7. Frequency

8. Safety precautions and clothing

9. Who is responsible with space for them to sign acceptance of responsibility.

10. Method for assessing cleaning effectiveness, details on monitoring and recording.

11. Integration with cleaning of surrounding / neighbouring areas. For example there is no point in cleaning equipment if a pressure washer will be used nearby which could lead to re-contamination.

5.8 Cleaning Out of Place - COP

Open surfaces and many items of equipment can be best cleaned and disinfected by disassembly or removal from its normal location in a process known as Cleaning Out of Place (COP as opposed to CIP).

The stages involved in cleaning are essentially, those outlined in Table 5.2, although there is a greater operator involvement and input of human mechanical energy than in CIP. It is inevitable that this type of cleaning is labour intensive. The complexity of COP ranges from the washing of equipment in sinks e.g. in catering operations, to the cleaning of quite large items of equipment using foams or gels in food manufacturing units.

Equipment for COP should be designed for food sanitation and constructed appropriately (see Table 5.3). Equipment should be easily cleaned with no gaps, crevices, exposed screw heads. Handles should be solid or hollows with sealed ends.

Equipment should be ergonomically designed to minimise operator fatigue.

Care should be taken to ensure COP equipment does not cause cross contamination. It should be selected carefully, maintained and cleaned properly and disposed of when worn or appropriate parts replaced.

Table 5.3 Materials used to construct cleaning equipment

MATERIAL	
Mild Steel	Used in frameworks and panelling needs to be protected from corrosion e.g. paint. Corrosion can cause paint to flake and enter food.
Stainless Steel	More expensive, more resistant to corrosion
Aluminium	Light in weight. Surface can corrode and become pitted. Avoid using alkaline cleaners and hypochlorites.
Plastics	Wide variety of plastics generally less expensive. Lighter in weight, don't corrode and relatively resistant to acids, alkalis and heat. Can cause foreign bodies if brittle.
Wood	Avoid, even in wooden handle brushes. Wood is porous and difficult to sanitise and dry.

5.8.1 Application of Energy in COP

Thermal or heat energy can be up to 80°C in some high temperature sinks / dish washers but is lower in hot water rinses (except steam). Chemical energy can be provided by means of detergents and alkalis.

Mechanical / kinetic energy can be applied in a variety of ways and to a greater or lesser extent. Simple "elbow power" is important in sink washing. Greater mechanical energy in the form of mechanical scrubbing is important in the cleaning of floors or other large flat areas and the machines may be fitted with a vacuum system to leave a dry surface. Increasing use is made in food manufacturing of pressure hoses and sprays with pressure generated centrally or by portable units.

These can be used to apply water and detergents under pressure and thus impart mechanical energy. They can be classified as low pressure high volume (LPHV) or high pressure low volume (HPLV). LPHV systems typically work at 3.5 to 5 bar with flow rates of approximately 450 litres per minute and can be fitted with different types of outlet nozzles giving different spray patterns depending on what is being cleaned.

Hot water can be used and this may be generated by mixing with steam. HPLV systems work generally in the range 40-100+ bar with flow rates between 5-80 litres per minute. Excessively high pressures can damage equipment/surface finishes.

Water under pressure hits objects with force and this removes more firmly adhering soil. However, this can also scatter the soil, water and any contaminant organisms over quite a wide area and should not be allowed to re-contaminate neighbouring clean areas. The pressure drops as the distance from the nozzle increases and is approximately 50% less at a distance of 300mm (12ins) and operators should use the pressure hoses at the correct distances specified in the cleaning schedule.

5.8.2 Equipment Used in COP

Equipment used in COP is summarised in Table 5.4 Of importance is the range of devices to ensure the addition of the correct amount of detergent to wash water. They prevent overdosing, reduce labour time and ensure consistency. Tap proportioners draw detergent by water action from a container. The level of suction is proportional to the flow of water therefore a constant concentration of water to detergent is ensured. A range of other dispensers including swan neck, bellows dispensers (wall mounted) are also used for dispensing detergents.

5.9 Cleaning In Place (CIP)

In food manufacturing plants, usually with extensive pipework (breweries, dairies) CIP has replaced COP (see Table 5.5). The basic cleaning cycle (see Table 5.6) is the same but non foaming chemicals and water are circulated through the process equipment in an assembled state. Detergents provide chemical energy, hot water provides thermal energy and water flow (velocity) in pipework generates turbulence and the use of pressure jets imparts mechanical energy. The use of heat can help to remove some soils and then disinfect but it can change the nature of the soil (e.g. melts fats).

5.9.1 Types of CIP Systems

A range of different types exist but generally they can be categorised as simple use, partial recovery and re-use. All require storage tanks for water and chemicals, process control equipment for management, valves to control liquid flow and sensing devices to detect levels. Single use systems are generally the smallest and simplest, cleaning solutions are discharged as effluent after use. The CIP is usually close to the equipment being cleaned and typically detergents with a short active life are used.

In some cases water from the intermediate or final rinse is used for the following cycle's pre-rinse stage.

Table 5.4 Types of Equipment Used in COP

Dispensing / Dosing Aids	Hand spraying, tap proportioners, backpack sprayers used to apply detergents and disinfectants at correct concentration.
Clothes / Wipes	Durable to disposable, with or without impregnated antibacterial agents. Reusable cloths can be important vehicles of contamination especially in catering and relating operations. Disposable cloth or paper towels minimise risk of cross contamination.
Brushes	Modern construction brushes are made from high density polypropylene often with coloured polyester bristles (easily visible). Worn brushes must be avoided and all brushes disinfected and dried after use. Can be colour coded to reduce cross contamination and be fitted with long handles.
Mops	Must be cleaned and disinfected regularly and stored dry. Detachable heads more easily disinfected after use.
Mechanical Scrapers	Useful in removing thick soils e.g. in baking, confectionery work. Should be made from tough plastic (metal ones can scratch / score surfaces).
Tanks / Sinks	Vary in size from small to large and in construction. Should be smoothly lined, no crevices curved corners and self draining. Can be plastic or food grade stainless steel.
Washing Machines	Vary from domestic type to large tunnel dish washers. Initial removal of gross debris important. High temperature can be used for disinfection but may "bake on" some types of food soil e.g. proteins.

Table 5.5 Advantages and Disadvantages of CIP compared to COP.

Advantages	
Economy - running costs	Optimum use of water, chemicals etc. combined with recycling. Plant down time is usually less, improved productivity. Less manual effort, much greater automation.
Safety -	Chemicals used in closed systems, less need for operators to clean inside vessels / tanks etc.
Efficacy -	Greater automation means dilutions likely to be more accurate / consistent, time / temperature process controlled for greater consistency. Care needed in setting up to ensure all areas cleaned. Automated 'on-line' ATP monitoring now available
Disadvantages	
High Initial Costs -	More expensive to design and install.
Maintenance -	Sophisticated, high maintenance costs
Flexibility -	Less flexible especially if process changes - pipework modified. Not so good on heavy soiled equipment. Re-use systems recycle water and cleaning components. An effective pre-rinse is important in all CIP systems to remove most of the soil but is particularly necessary in re-use systems to ensure the re-used detergent will be effective. Single use and re-use are compared in table 5.6.

How to Clean

Table 5.6 Typical CIP Cycle

Step	Reason	Single Use CIP (Typical)	Re-Use CIP (Typical)
Preliminary Rinse - or hot water	Removes gross soil	3 pre rinses of approx. 20 seconds, water discharged to drain	5 mins at ambient using re-cycled water
Detergent Wash time, temperature and concentration are important	Removes residual debris and scale	Hot water and detergent approx. 10-15 mins, discharge to drain	20°- 85°C for 10 mins recycled for further use
Intermediate Rinse	Removes detergent residues	Approx. 1 min discharge or use for next cycle's pre-rinse	Ambient temperature for 3 mins
Disinfection	Destroys micro-organisms	Discharge	Recycle
Final rinse good microbiological quality water needed	Removes disinfectant	Cold water approx. 3 mins	Cold water approx. 3 mins

5.9.2 Important Factors in CIP Systems

To be successful the CIP system needs to be carefully designed and the factors to be considered are summarised in Table 5.7.

Table 5.7 Factors Important in the Success of CIP Systems

Pipework	Flow through pipework should generate turbulence. Flow velocity should not be excessive and typically 1.5-2m/s. Pipework needs to be designed to minimise dead legs and have good drainage.
Vessels / Tanks	Smooth sided with good easy drainage to avoid accumulation of old solutions. Vessels can be cleaned with low flow high pressure jets which move over and cover the inside of the vessel. This approach is useful for heavy soiling due to the imparting of mechanical energy to knock off the soil. An alternative is the use of high flow low pressure applied via sprayballs. The liquid is sprayed onto the roof / upper sides of the vessel creating a falling trickle of liquid which covers the whole inside surface. Chemical energy (detergent) is particularly important in removing the soil.
Sprayballs	Relatively durable with no moving parts, self draining, continuous coverage in operation.
Rotating Jets	More expensive with variable reliability not always self draining, intermittent coverage, impart higher mechanical energy.

Chapter 6. ASSESSING CLEANLINESS - MANAGEMENT CONTROL

6.1 Background

Cross contamination has been reported as a contributory factor in 38% of cases of food poisoning but even this may be a serious under estimate. Unclean surfaces are likely to be an important factor in cross contamination as well as being an important determinant of product quality and shelf life. Cleaning, including disinfection, should reduce the number of microorganisms on a food surface to an acceptable level. This importance coupled with the cost of cleaning means it should be validated, monitored and verified to ensure maximum effectiveness at minimum cost.

Unfortunately in many food premises evaluation of cleaning is either absent or poorly performed. Assessment of cleaning should be evaluated against hygiene requirements and should lead to the production of an integrated cleaning assessment strategy. The approach used in this strategy is likely to be a combination of microbiological, visual and other non microbiological methods (see Fig. 6.1, 6.5 and 6.8).

Surfaces or alternatively (especially for CIP systems) rinse water can be tested. The best people to perform the assessment will vary from plant to plant depending upon the Quality Assurance processes but assessment should be documented and verified either within GMP, HACCP or ISO 9000 systems.

Fig. 6.1 Assessing Surface Hygiene

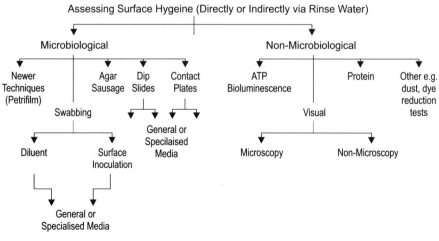

Source adapted from ref. 10

Table 6.1 Factors Influencing the Choice of Assessment Method

FACTOR	COMMENT
Cost	Cost of cleaning and the assessment of cleaning efficiency must be optimised especially for designated critical control points. This may include capital as well as running costs.
Time	The speed with which results are required. For a designated critical control point this should be in time for corrective action to be taken. Speed of results may be especially important in a 24 hour production environment.
Information Required	Is information on residual surface microorganisms needed or is the level of surface cleanliness (including product debris / biofilms and microorganisms) more important? Is information on specific organisms e.g. coliforms needed?
Staff	Level of technical training
Ease of Use	Considered in relation to availability of technical staff
Type of Product & Predicted Level of Contamination	Levels of cleanliness required and amount of monitoring needed can be product related. They must be considered in relation to sensitivity and limits of detection required and possible levels of contamination.
Position in Plant	Do surfaces need to be checked as part of GMP or are they CCPs? Consider in relation to other CCPs and processing methods.
Reliability, repeatability & reproducibility	Does the test give reliable and reproducible results. Are target values and critical limits required, if so can they be achieved?
Management Needs	Requirements for due diligence defence, second or third party audits.
Nature of Food Contact Surface	The composition and shape of the surfaces being monitored may influence the selection of hygiene monitoring methods.

Source adapted from ref. 10

Table 6.2 Comparison of Main Microbiological Cultivation Methods for Assessing Cleanliness

	ADVANTAGES	DISADVANTAGES
Swabbing	Widely used and accepted Can be qualitative (specific organisms) and quantitative. Any shape, size or surface can be tested Relatively inexpensive. Test itself quick and easy to perform Mechanical energy imparted giving better pick-up from biofilms Dilutions can be made thus more quantitative for heavily contaminated surfaces	Often poorly executed and implemented. Lack of standardised protocol. Methods, media etc. may vary widely Incubation and sterilisation facilities or outside laboratory needed. Staff with some microbiological training needed. Indirect method via a swab, often poor pickup, especially from dry surfaces. Motile organisms can cover surface of agar
Contact	Direct contact with surface Better pick-up of transient contaminants. Fixed area Better repeatability Can be bought pre-prepared Available in variety of media Relatively inexpensive Test is quick and easy to perform	Flat smooth surfaces only Poorer pick-up from biofilms Motile organisms can cover surface of agar Possible agar residue on surface Lids can become detached in transport Incubation & sterilisation facilities needed. Overgrowth from heavily contaminated surfaces
Dip Slide	Direct contact with surface Better repeatability Fixed area / Narrow shape Better pick-up of transient organisms Can be bought pre-prepared Available in a variety of media Different media on reverse side of paddle if required Minimal incubation facilities needed (Incupot - portable incubator) Can be used to test rinse water Sealed unit with screw cap Longer shelf life. Paddle can be hinged for easier use Quick and easy to perform	Flat smooth surfaces only Poor pick-up from biofilms Motile organisms can cover surface of agar Incubation and sterilisation or disinfection facilities needed Possible agar residue on surface Overgrowth from heavily contaminated surface Source adapted from ref. 10

Table 6.3 Comparison of 'In-House'and External Microbiological Assessment

ATTRIBUTE	IN HOUSE	EXTERNAL
Cost	High capital outlay (£2000+) Lower running costs - 60-90p per sample The greater the number of tests the more cost effective	No capital outlay. Running costs £5 - £17 per swab. External laboratories must make a profit. Costs of transportation. Can be more cost effective for small operations. May be discount for large number of samples
Safety	Organisms and possible pathogens may be cultivated in the same building as the food production environment.	Organism cultivated in site remote from production
Speed	Quick availability of results	May be a delay in results. Time for transportation.
Methodology	May or may not be standardised. Laboratory may or may not be accredited. May not be cost effective to introduce sophisticated new techniques	Increasingly laboratories are required to be externally accredited e.g. NAMAS. Standard methods likely to be used. Can use the latest sophisticated techniques of analysis - sensitivity, economy of scale
Acceptance	Results may or may not be accepted by third party.	Results more likely to be accepted by third party.
Transport of Swab	Minimal time delay between sampling and analysis. More immediate response to problems.	Variable delay due to transport, may result in loss of viability of organisms. Transport methodology may need validation to demonstrate no loss in viability
Staffing	Technically trained staff needed by company, may be more highly motivated than in external laboratories. In-house staff more knowledgeable of product, expected flora etc. In-house staff less likely to misunderstand requirements. Technical expertise can be an asset to the comapny.	Technically trained staff provided by external laboratory External staff have no knowledge of product and sample sites etc. Mistakes in communications can occur. Dialogue with an 'expert' may cost additional money. Source adapted from ref. 10

Table 6.4 Comparison of Microbiological and NonMicrobiological Assessment Methods

ATTRIBUTE	MICROBIOLOGICAL (Cultivation)	ATP	PROTEIN
Acceptance	Accepted by food industry world wide	Widely accepted in UK, USA, & some other countries. Less well used & accepted elsewhere. Acceptance increasing rapidly.	Accepted in Japan. Only recently introduced to the UK.
Method / principle tested	Microorganisms derived from surface grow and multiply. Allows accurate identification of contaminant organisms. Laboratory facilities required.	ATP derived from microorganisms and food debris analysed using a luminometer. ATP can be assessed directly on surface or indirectly via a swab. No laboratory facilities needed.	Protein from surface food debris transferred to a swab. Protein detected by an enhanced Biuret reaction and compared to colour card. No instrumentation. No laboratory facilities needed.
Time for results	18 - 48 hours	2 minutes	10-15 minutes
Sensitivity to a standard raw milk suspension	Inferior to luminometry	Superior and improving	Inferior to microbiological and ATP
Typical Limits of Bacterial Detection: Wet Surfaces [+] Dry Surfaces [+] Wet Surfaces [++] Dry Surfaces [++]	$10^5/10^4$ $10^6/10^7$ 10^2 $10^5/10^7$	10^4 10^4	$> 10^7$ $> 10^7$
Reproductibility for raw milk contaminated surface	CV 84 - 300%	CV 9-79%	Not applicable due to type of results
Approximate running cost	60-100p (In-house)	95-185p	95p
Capital cost	Variable but incubator £130-£2000 Autoclave £600-£10,000	£1500-£4000 Discounts and trade-ins possible	Zero
Staff Requirements	Some level of microbiological training preferable	Relatively little training	Relatively little training

[+] Diluent Spread Plates   [++] Direct Streaking   CV Coefficient of Variation

Source adapted from ref. 10

6.2 Techniques to Assess Cleanliness Sensory / Visual

Visual examination / inspection after cleaning can reveal gross deficiencies - if this happens other forms of testing are relatively pointless on visually unclean surfaces. Normally, visual assessment can only reveal residual food soil. In a small number of cases microbial growth may be observed (e.g. mould on food soil in bakeries). Visual examination can also be performed after wetting a dry surface to observe water dispersion, indicating possible grease residues. Dry paper tissues wiped over a surface can also indicate residual grease or fat. All visual examinations should be carried out in well-lit conditions. In some cases "smelling" the surface can indicate residual and or deteriorating product (e.g. beer, dairy products).

Visual assessment should not be confined to flat open surfaces. Mirrors and even fibre-optic exploration can be used to assess hidden or out of the way places. Hidden and difficult to clean areas can harbour biofilms and are often the cause of contamination problems. In CIP systems specific visual inspection sites can be designed into the system.

Visual examination can be improved by the use of microscopy including direct epifluorescent filter techniques (DEFT) and direct epifluorescent microscopy (DEM). These methods can be used to observe bacteria on surfaces but are impractical for most food producers.

Visual examination is therefore often the first stage in an integrated assessment strategy. It detects gross deficiencies due to the presence of visible food soil but without magnification cannot normally be used as an assessment of disinfection.

6.3 Techniques to Assess Cleanliness - ATP Bioluminescence

ATP bioluminescence is a rapid means of assessing cleanliness and is likely to be the second stage in many assessment strategies (see Figs 6.5-6.8). This technique measures the amount of total organic soil on a surface including microorganisms and food debris. Both contain ATP (adenosine triphosphate) and thus a surface free from these is low in ATP. The test uses an extractant and an enzyme system, firefly luciferin: luciferase, to convert the ATP into light which is then measured in a luminometer. Surfaces which are clean have little ATP and will produce a low light emission. Surfaces which are unclean have ATP present and this will be measured in relative light units (RLU) as a higher emission of light.   Although this approach does not measure microorganisms per se, "modernists" argue it represents a better test of cleaning. They also argue that even if a surface is unclean due to food debris, rather than microrganisms, then the food debris will soon become the focus for microbial growth and present a contamination risk. An analysis of the ATP found on food contact surfaces reveals it is typically 20-40% microbial and 80-60% food debris in origin. However it is possible to have ATP readings which can be nearly all microbial in origin or nearly all food debris in origin.

Over the past decade the use of ATP bioluminescence has increased considerably and the predictions are that this increase will continue. ATP assessment is compared with other techniques in Table 6.4. However its key advantage is that it gives results within minutes thus providing "real time" data and an opportunity to reclean if the results indicate inadequate cleaning. This allows the technique to provide rapid validation test results as well as being useful within monitoring. Several studies have compared the results gained from microbiological and ATP bioluminescence methods for assessing "in situ" surface cleanliness. In most cases there appeared to be a good correlation (see also Fig 6.4) although it must be remembered that they are measuring different things. The former detects only microorganisms the latter is a measure of total organic soil, therefore they do not necessarily correlate.

ATP is easy to use and provides more repeatable and reproducible results than microbiological testing. Optimum methods of microbiological testing offer better detectability on wet surfaces but ATP is better at detecting microorganisms on dry surfaces see Table 6.4. The technique can be susceptible to quenching (reduced response due to residual disinfectant) although this can now be positively tested for. The technique has also been adapted for continuous monitoring of CIP rinse waters. Depending on the make of instrument selected it can also be used as the platform for a range of additional QA tests including phosphatase, antibiotics, pesticides etc.

Although not routinely carried out, it is possible, using additional reagents provided by one manufacturer to distinguish between microbial and non microbial ATP. This can be of great value and should be used more widely as it provides information as to which aspect of cleaning / disinfection has not been carried out appropriately.

6.4 Techniques to Assess Cleanliness - Protein
Tests based upon protein estimation have recently become available. These tests are relatively rapid (approx. 15 mins) but are not capable of detecting low levels of food soil especially if this has a low protein content. As such they have only provided a crude estimate of cleanliness and this should be considered in relation to cost. However, developments in protein detection are leading to quicker, easier and more sensitive tests. It is claimed these now offer a better indication to microbial surface counts.

6.5 Techniques to Assess Cleanliness - Microbiological testing

The traditional method of measuring cleanliness is based upon microbial enumeration (counts) expressed as either an aerobic plate count (APC), aerobic colony count (ACC) or colony forming units (cfu). The term Total Viable Count (TVC) is less correct but often used in the food industry. However it is possible to have a surface contaminated with food soil having a low microbial count at the time of testing which would, using such methods, show up as clean. Traditionalists would, nevertheless, argue that it is only microorganisms that are a hazard and microbial enumeration is the best method for determining their level. It is, however, the need to cultivate microorganisms that is the main downfall of this traditional approach, results are not available for 24-48 hours.

Various methods of enumerating microbial surface contamination exist although there is no consensus as to which is the best. Table 6.2 summarises their main advantages and disadvantages. They can be broadly split into 2 approaches, those based upon swabbing and those based upon direct contact with the growth medium. Swabbing and plate counting can provide qualitative and quantitative information on the microorganisms present. Unfortunately the technique does not offer high levels of repeatability or reproducibility. After touching the surface, swabs can be used to inoculate the surface of an agar plate directly or immersed in a diluent prior to enumeration. Swabs can vary in size, larger swabs may have a better recovery but lack precision. Alternatives to swabs in the form of sterile sponges or gauzes are available. All require microbiological laboratory facilities. A key decision to be taken in microbiological testing relates to timing of testing and wetness of the surface. Bacteria dried onto a surface are more difficult to remove and testing of dried surfaces will usually give a much lower result.

An alternative approach is to use dip slides or contact plates. These touch the surface to be tested, or in the case of dip slides rinse waters also, and microorganisms from the surface contaminate the agar on which they subsequently grow to produce colonies. One area of debate is whether it is better to use swabs or contact plates / dip slides for testing in food plants. Although there is conflicting evidence it seems that dip slides/contact plates are better for low levels of transient contaminants whereas swabbing, because of the input of mechanical energy, is better for testing areas where biolfilms have formed or heavy contamination has occurred.

An advantage of microbiological testing is that in addition to generalised growth media, specialised or selective media to look for specific types of organisms, can be used. General and specialised media can be used as a source of colonies allowing accurate identification of any contaminant bacteria.   Neutralising agents can be incorporated into the agar to counter the effects of residual disinfectants.   A problem of increasing concern relates to viable but non culturable organisms (VNBC).   These are bacteria which after exposure to disinfectants, heat or other stress factors may be injured and although still viable they cannot be easily cultivated.   This can give a false impression of a low number of residual viable organisms.

Most methods of microbiological testing are of value in the assessment of cleaning, either in validation or in the testing of surfaces found to have a high ATP reading.

6.6 Rinses and Rinse Water Testing

Previous sections have considered the direct sampling of surfaces either using swabs or direct contact.   An alternative method and one of particular benefit in CIP systems is the testing of rinse water which is a reflection of the cleanliness of surfaces in contact with the rinse waters. Bacteria suspended in sterile rinses or rinse waters can be concentrated by filtration or directly analysed.   Methods for analysis include microbial examination using DEFT, microbial cultivation or ATP based methods.   The latter can involve standard ATP approaches or a new high sensitivity approach which involves adenylate kinase (AK).

This method utilises a continuous flow luminometer,   which splits the incoming sample equally, one determining total ATP and the other free ATP in the rinse water. The difference between these is the amount of microbial ATP.   This technique claims to have a number of advantages and provides detailed, instant and even on-line analysis of the water circulating in a CIP system (see Fig 6.2 and 6.3).   The technique is likely to find widespread use in the beverage and brewing industries, dairy industry and in food plants where large amounts of water are used and even recycled e.g. poultry processing.   Using high sensitivity reagents this technique has a lower detection limit of 10^3 bacterial cells/ml.

Fig. 6.2 Autotrack Profile of Effective CIP Cleaning Process of 'Product Holding Tank'.

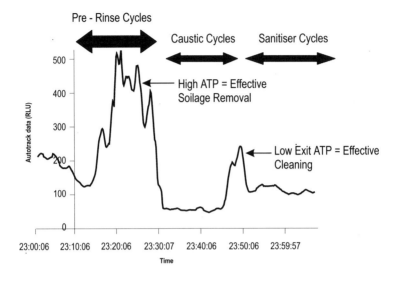

Fig. 6.3 Autotrack Profile of Defective CIP Cleaning Process Of 'Product Holding Tank'.

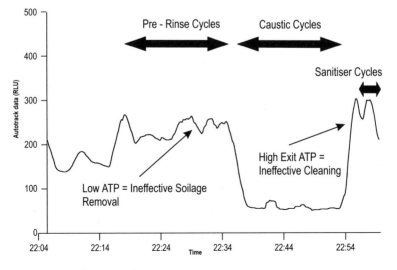

Source: Biotrace PLC.

6.7 Validating A Cleaning Programme

At the design stage, particularly at designated critical control points, cleaning should be validated. This requires the production of evidence to show that the cleaning process is capable of delivering an appropriate level of cleanliness and an acceptable residual level of microorganisms under a variety of working conditions. Remembering that they test different things, ATP bioluminescence and microbiological methods can be used, not only to test the surface at the end of cleaning, but also after the separate component stages. This allows the testing of the efficacy of different temperatures, rinse times, detergents or disinfectants to obtain maximum effect for minimum cost. Research at the validation stage can not only result in a more effective cleaning programme but also considerable savings on heat or chemicals.

Figure 6.4 shows validation results obtained from different cleaning schedules involving 3, 4, 5 or 6 stages. Target values in cfu / $100cm^2$ and RLU / $100cm^2$ have been set as well as upper limits for marginally acceptable. In this particular example a 5/6 stage cleaning process gave all results (n=5) clearly in the pass zone. A 3 /4 stage process (without disinfection) failed or was only marginally acceptable. In this instance to meet target values a 5/6 stage process needs to be adopted.

6.8 Monitoring a Cleaning Programme

Monitoring is a planned series of observations or measurements of a named parameter. After cleaning has taken place, measurements (visual plus ATP or microbial) should be taken to ensure that it has been carried out correctly or to an appropriate standard. Figs. 6.5 to 6.8 illustrate how a combination of methods can be used to provide a strategic approach to hygiene monitoring for a range of food operations. This type of approach requires the setting of target values and critical limits. Target values are those obtained regularly after cleaning has been fully and correctly performed and when the cleaning programme has been validated. Critical limits represent the upper measurement limits you are prepared to accept. Setting target values and critical limits requires repeated testing to enable statistically based values to be established. If visual assessments are used a clear description of what is acceptable or unacceptable, supported by diagrams or photographs if necessary, should be provided. If monitoring results in a "fail" then the reason for this happening and how a repetition could be prevented needs to be investigated. See cause and effect analysis in Appendix 2.

Results from monitoring should be documented and used in trend analysis. This requires results to be reviewed and analysed at regular intervals or when results approach critical limits. This type of data, coupled with additional testing and, if necessary, observation of cleaning operatives to see that schedules are correctly implemented, is useful in verification and could help to establish a due diligence defence.

Fig 6.4 Validating a Cleaning Programme using ATP Bioluminescence (in RLU's) and Microbiological Swabbing (cfu)

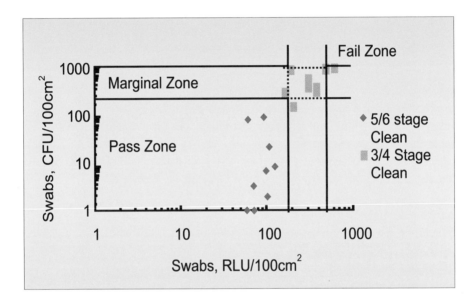

Notes on Figure 6.4 Validation of a Cleaning Programme

Stainless steel contact surface was evenly inoculated with ice-cream, contaminated with 1×10^6 of a mixed inoculum, left in contact for 1 hour.

3 stage clean: Initial rinse, detergent wash, final rinse
4 stage clean: as above plus 60 minute dry
5 stage clean: as 3 stage + terminal disinfectant + rinse
6 stage clean: as 5 stage + 60 minute dry
Each point is mean of 5 determinations.

Source ref. 22

6.9 Clean Surface Specifications

It is difficult to prescribe standards or target values for surface cleanliness for two reasons, much depends upon what is practicable given the cleaning routines and the condition of the surface and because the desirable level will depend upon what the surface is used for and the type of product. Additionally, the methods used for testing and the wetness of the surface can also affect the setting of target values. Nevertheless surfaces that cannot be cleaned satisfactorily should be replaced. Specified levels of cleanliness are especially important at critical control points (CCPs). Surfaces in contact with high risk products (i.e. those that support microbial growth and will receive little or no further processing) are likely to be CCPs and need to have a very low level of residual microbial contamination and be free from pathogens after cleaning.

Target values / specifications need therefore to be determined for each plant and each site. Even if the same site is sampled repeatedly there will be variation in the results. Therefore after thorough cleaning, using a validated programme, repeated values at a specific site should be determined using a standard testing protocol. This enables a typical mean value to be calculated. To set an upper critical limit this value plus 2 standard deviations (SD) or 2 standard error of the mean (SEM) or the mean plus 20% or other methods can be used depending upon the degree of stringency required.

With this is mind some previously suggested target values and critical limits are illustrated in Table 6.5.

In setting target values it should be remembered that often bacteria are not "normally distributed". Therefore the sampling area should be large enough to minimise this effect and should ideally be at least $100 cm^2$. However where surfaces are not flat the sampling protocol should specify exactly what is to be tested. This may be the entire surface e.g. tap handle or only the parts likely to be touched. Similarly detailed descriptions should be provided for irregular surfaces. It may be mathematically preferable to describe microbiological counts in terms of the $\log_{10}$ as this minimises the effect of a small number of high counts in setting mean values.

Results from monitoring should be used in trend analysis. Computer software can be especially helpful and it may be possible to identify areas of poor cleaning or when cleaning is likely to go out of control. The latest luminometers have sophisticated trend analysis software incorporated into them, making security and downloading of information much easier.

Table 6.5 Some Suggested Target Values for Surfaces after Cleaning

Microbiological (in cfu)		
Canneries	Satisfactory Acceptable Unacceptable	$<540/100cm^2$ $540\text{-}2700/100cm^2$ $>2700/100cm^2$
Dairy	Target	$<100/100cm^2$
Meat Industry	Target	$<800/100cm^2$
Food Service Industry (Contact Surface)	Target	$<1000/100cm^2$
Fridge Handle (Food Service Industry)	Target	$<5000/100cm^2$
ATP Bioluminescence (in RLU)		
Chopping Board (Food Service)	Target Upper Limit	<500 >750
Stainless Steel Surface (Food Manufacturer)	Target Upper Limit	<250 >350

Fig. 6.5 Stages in an Integrated Cleaning Monitoring Programme
Small Catering or Retail Operation

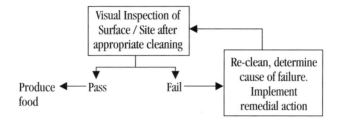

Fig. 6.6 Stages in an Integrated Cleaning Monitoring Programme -
Large Catering or Retail Operation

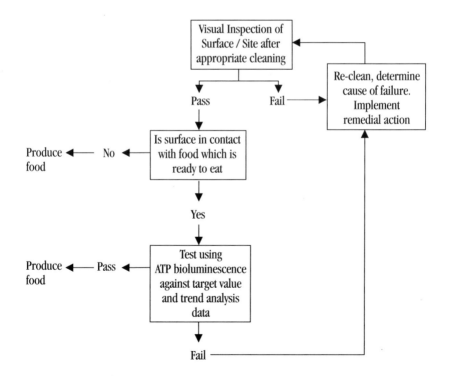

Fig. 6.7 Stages in an Integrated Cleaning Monitoring Programme-
Medium Sized Food Manufacturer or Large National Retailer

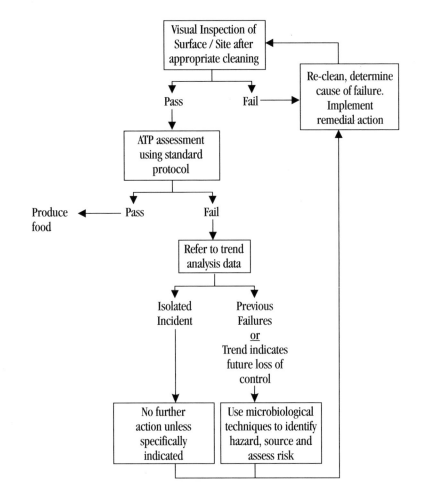

How to Clean

Figure 6.8 Stages in an Integrated Cleaning Monitoring Programme -
Large Food Manufacturer (or medium size with strong commitment to cleaning)
Producing Processed Foods.

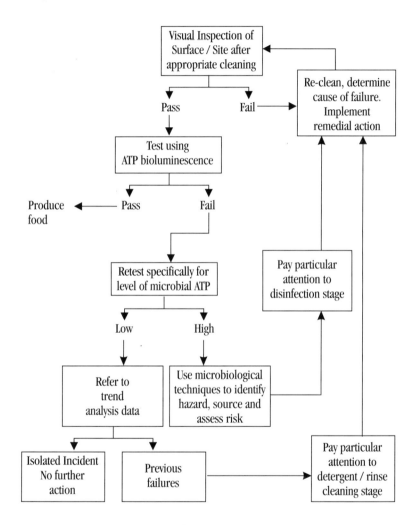

Chapter 7. PRACTICAL DEVELOPMENT OF A CLEANING PROGRAMME
- A Manufacturing Example

7.1 Constructing a Cleaning Plan

The company may design its own plan or contract specialist support to both design and operate the plan. The example provided gives guidance in designing and validating a new or existing plan.

7.2 Making your Survey

A site survey report should be produced which

- identifies each area in the factory
- identifies each key item in an area, environment, surfaces and vectors
- allocates a frequency of cleaning for areas and items
- recommends a sequence of cleaning to prevent re-contamination
- recommends standard cleaning procedures for the area or individual items from trade asociation experience or supply companies.

Fig. 7.1 A simple Review Sheet used to Capture Information Prior to Installing a Plan

For: Packing/Trimming	SHAMROCK SITE SURVEY REPORT								Date:- 1.1.2000	
Frequency →										
Key Items etc.	Mon	Tues	Wed	Thur	Fri	Sat	Sun	Checklist	Yes No	Comments
Doors	✗	✗	✗	✗	✗			Sufficient water	✓	Lack of water pressure
Walls	✗	✗	✗	✗	✗			Special adaptors	✓	Incorrect water fittings
Floors	✗	✗	✗	✗	✗			Electric supply	✓	Exposed electrical fittings
Ceilings	CLEAN MONTHLY							Adaptors	✓	Need to connect to 3 phase
Tables	Clean as you go (CAYG)							Sufficient Drainage	✓	Pools of water present
Knives	CAYG							Extraction Fans	✓	Blocked extraction fan
Boards	CAYG							Ventilation	✓	Poor
Brushes	CAYG							Exposed fixtures	✓	Telephone connections exposed
Pads	CAYG							Additional eqpt	✓	Steam unit
								Approx time	✓	8 man hours / night
								Approx cost		£2000 / month

(Sequence ↓)

Additional problems noted	Suggested Changes	Timescale for action
Deadleg in Pipework	re-configure	5 days
Worn & pitted surface	replace with new	5 days
Workflow cross-contamination	re-organise	30 days

The area of the factory identified for cleaning is Packing, Trimming and Weighing which is shown on Fig 7.2

Figure 7.1 provides the manager with a document upon which a plan can be constructed. We can see that the manager can also note any special "limitations" or requirements of the area. Notes given in the far right hand column are explained in Table 7.1 These are the other factors which should be collected when building the cleaning plan and capture the limitations of the area or item to be cleaned.

Table 7.1 Key Points to Note When Planning Cleaning are as Follows

Check	Problem noted	Action
Water	Insufficient water pressure	New water point
Water Adapters	Special fittings required	Ensure available for crew
Electrical supply	Exposed fixtures e.g.insectocutors non- sealed sockets back of socket not sealed to wall sockets or lights on roof	Identify , instructions to crew (ITC) Seal were possible- spring covers Instructions to electrician not sealed inside roof -(ITC)
Electrical adapters	Supply, single or three phase	Clearly identify -make plugs available
Drainage	Insufficient drainage	Modify drains- ensure no pools remain
Extraction fan	Blocked extraction fan	Ensure available and adequate
Ventilation	Poor ventilation during cleaning	Ensure masks available for crew
Exposed fixtures	Phone points video cameras	Exposed -set back in wall Exposed - ITC
Additional eqpt	Note special equipment for area or items	Vacuum cleaner, steam unit
Approx. time	Suggest time to clean area in man hrs	Confirm time and effectiveness
Estimate Cost	Cost chemicals , water and equipment	Confirm usage over next month

7.3 Operating Plan - Shamrock Fisheries

The company now has a provisional "plan" to clean a new area or item of equipment. The main issues relating to the practicality of the cleaning have been logged and potential problems minimised through planning. The company may operate a single procedure which involves cleaning an area with suitable instructions to hand scrub specific items. Alternatively individual cleaning procedures may be issued for main items. We will now review the cleaning schedule and procedures of a fictional company

Fig. 7.2 Shamrock Factory Site Layout Work Flow

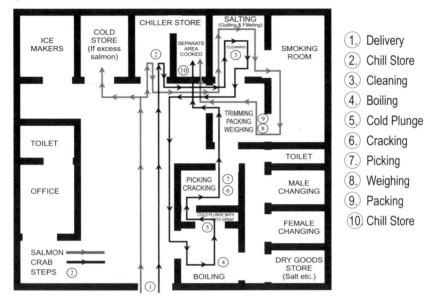

7.3.1 Cleaning - The Whole Area Approach

Using review sheets in Fig. 7.1 major items have been recorded and the frequency of clean has been set based on an assessment of the risk and normal industrial practice. The suggested frequency has been logged by marking the boxes underneath the days of the week and other frequencies noted in the comments box e.g. monthly, after each shift (AES) or clean as you go (CAYG) (see Fig 7.1). The cleaning sequence is given by the order in which the environment, items and vectors have been listed - usually cleaning the dirtiest areas first.

The manager has suggested that the crew begin by cleaning the environment followed by the food contact surfaces and finally cleaning equipment.

The practicality and consequences of these instructions will be discussed with the crew to prevent or minimise contamination of a previously cleaned item. Gross debris may be removed and then the area cleaned as one "item". The area and individual items may have unique cleaning procedures and then be protected from re-contamination either by careful cleaning, movement to a separate area where possible or protected after cleaning by plastic overwrap.

The cleaning procedure may be a "standard" for this type of environment , soil and equipment. Alternatively the procedure may be unique and need to be developed and then fully tested. Chapter 4 has described the nature of chemicals and the soils they are designed to remove. Chapter 6 and section 7.5 provides practical guidance in how to ensure cleaning is effective. The company may rely on the advice of the supply company to select chemicals with appropriate actions but should also ensure their functionality through plant trials. Another step the company may take is to ensure the chemicals have been "certified" through the national scheme e.g. the one operated by the Royal Institute of Public Health and Hygiene.

We can see that the frequency may vary from clean as you go (CAYG) to a monthly clean (Fig 7.3). A review of the flow chart (Fig 7.4) for the plant revealed that the final product chilling had been identified as a CCP. The cleaning plan for this chiller was therefore reviewed and the frequency modified.

The cleaning schedule of the process area was also reviewed in line with the HACCP plan and agreed by the team to be satisfactory. The visual observations and microbiological test results confirmed that the selected cleaning method was effective in reducing the target organisms to an agreed level.

Fig. 7.3 This is the cleaning schedule in place for the Chiller

Item	Freq	Doc	Rev
WALLS	Weekly	Chiller. WLS	1
FLOOR	Daily	Chiller. FLR	1
RACKING	Bi Weekly	Chiller. RCK	1
EVAPORATORS	Monthly	Chiller. EVP	1
DOOR - HANDLES	CAYG	Chiller. DOR	1
DOORS	Daily	Chiller. DOR	1

CLEANING SCHEDULE
Area: Process area

Fig. 7.4 Work Flow Chart

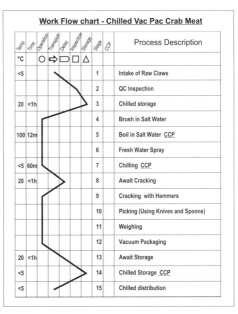

Work Flow chart - Chilled Vac Pac Crab Meat

Temp °C	Time		Process Description
<5		1	Intake of Raw Claws
		2	QC Inspection
20	<1h	3	Chilled storage
		4	Brush in Salt Water
100	12m	5	Boil in Salt Water CCP
		6	Fresh Water Spray
<5	60m	7	Chilling CCP
20	<1h	8	Await Cracking
		9	Cracking with Hammers
		10	Picking (Using Knives and Spoons)
		11	Weighing
		12	Vacuum Packaging
20	<1h	13	Await Storage
<5		14	Chilled Storage CCP
<5		15	Chilled distribution

7.3.2 Cleaning Plan Style

The initial plan was provided for the entire area of the factory with short instructions for dealing with small items. This style is normally appropriate for small companies producing low risk food using few chemicals - the expansion of the activities in the factory as shown in Fig 7.2 required a review of this approach. Fig 7.5 gives an overview of the cleaning procedures manual based on the area approach. We can see that this manual also contains a policy declaration, safety (COSHH) data, the schedules, procedures and justification that the procedures work. We will discuss validation further in section 7.4

Fig. 7.5 The "Power Cleen" Approach

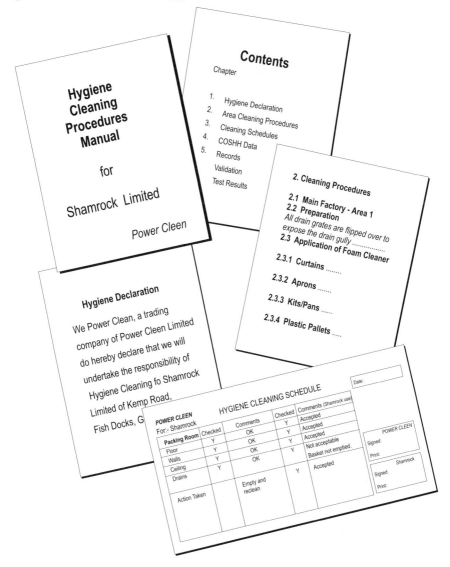

7.4 Modifying the Plan - Individual Procedures

The company had reviewed the existing cleaning plan and found that some items were being poorly cleaned and needed alternative chemicals or more detailed instructions for the crew

The factory team decided on the use of an alternative approach. This consisted of individual cards for each item of equipment. The procedure was initially divided into 3 sections which were.

- Cleaning equipment to be used- which ensured the crew had withdrawn what they needed from stores.

- Cleaning chemicals used- this provided the type of chemical they would use as well as simple instructions on make up.

- Cleaning method- key steps in cleaning method were then listed.

The new cards were laminated in plastic and could be taken into the process area as needed by the crew.

This provided detailed guidance for cleaning particular items.

7.4.1 Card System

The team operated the new cards and schedules for one month and then decided on the following modifications.

- Safe handling instructions should be added to the cleaning chemical section.

- Standard required and key risk areas should be added to the final section.

- Signature for completion of check should be added to the schedule.

An example of a card is provided in Fig 7.6, also see Appendix 4.

Fig. 7.6 Cleaning Card Procedure

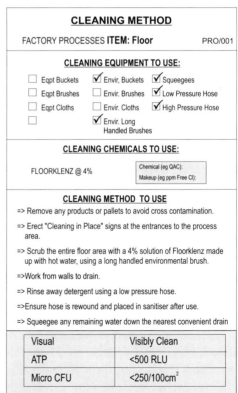

CLEANING METHOD

FACTORY PROCESSES **ITEM: Floor**   PRO/001

CLEANING EQUIPMENT TO USE:

☐ Eqpt Buckets	☑ Envir, Buckets	☑ Squeegees
☐ Eqpt Brushes	☐ Envir. Brushes	☑ Low Pressure Hose
☐ Eqpt Cloths	☐ Envir. Cloths	☑ High Pressure Hose
☐	☑ Envir. Long Handled Brushes	

CLEANING CHEMICALS TO USE:

FLOORKLENZ @ 4%   Chemical (eg QAC):
Makeup (eg ppm Free Cl):

CLEANING METHOD TO USE

=> Remove any products or pallets to avoid cross contamination.

=> Erect "Cleaning in Place" signs at the entrances to the process area.

=> Scrub the entire floor area with a 4% solution of Floorklenz made up with hot water, using a long handled environmental brush.

=>Work from walls to drain.

=> Rinse away detergent using a low pressure hose.

=>Ensure hose is rewound and placed in sanitiser after use.

=> Squeegee any remaining water down the nearest convenient drain

Visual	Visibly Clean
ATP	<500 RLU
Micro CFU	<250/100cm^2

7.4.2 Checking Performance

The manager and the cleaning crew are now satisfied that a plan is in place which results in a satisfactory clean as determined by the standard. The weekly meetings enable any problems to be highlighted from performance standards. A more detailed picture of the "hot spots" has been built up and added to the cleaning manual which is used for reference purposes and for training.

The team had designed a plan and developed documentation which was practical and worked for them. Simple records were maintained by :-

- Crew sign schedule to show cleaning of an area is complete - supervisor checks and countersigns

- Periodic check by manager to assess areas or items - specific checklist and procedure- records kept

- Routine ATP or microbiological test to confirm detergents and disinfectants work - records available

Additionally end product samples are also examined microbiologically from different parts of the product run to ensure no upward trends.

7.5 Proving It Works - Practical Approach to Validation

The team also recognised that many of the cleaning procedures were not validated - it was decided to develop an approach to validation . The factory decided to organise the existing information which they held to prove that the methods they used worked and this was done at four levels.

- **Traditional Control** - The existing cleaning methods were tried and tested within the company and throughout the industry. Previous end product microbiological results and plant surface data has shown no problems in using the procedures although no specific trials had been done.

- **Theoretical Control**- Data from the chemical company, or from specific references show that the named chemical has a defined action against the target organisms or in removal of a given soil.

- **Predicted Control** - This involves the use of microbiological models to show that a given chemical will prevent growth or destroy a target organism.

- **Plant Trials** - Specific trials undertaken in the factory to prove a procedure or chemical has achieved the predicted or theoretical result, in practice.

7.5.1 Validation Manual

Figure 7.7 gives an overview of the Validation manual developed by the company. We can see it contains a structured mechanism for collecting the existing information available in the company , industry, supplier and literature to prove their cleaning plan should work. If they feel that the theoretical evidence and trade information is not sufficiently clear then employing predictive models and undertaking plant trials may be the next option but only after level 1 and 2 are complete. For low risk areas this level of validation may be sufficient.

Fig. 7.7 Example of contents of Validation Manual (see Appendix)

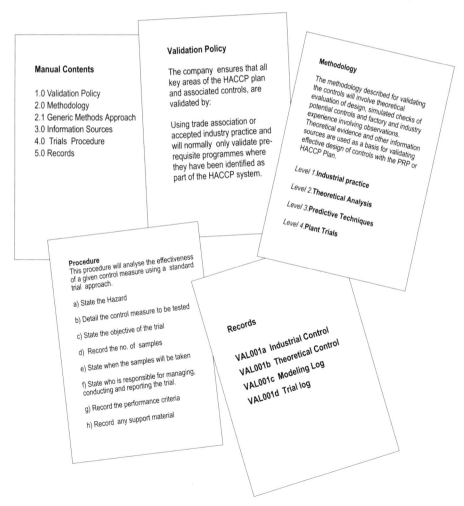

Manual Contents

1.0 Validation Policy
2.0 Methodology
2.1 Generic Methods Approach
3.0 Information Sources
4.0 Trials Procedure
5.0 Records

Validation Policy

The company ensures that all key areas of the HACCP plan and associated controls, are validated by:

Using trade association or accepted industry practice and will normally only validate pre-requisite programmes where they have been identified as part of the HACCP system.

Methodology

The methodology described for validating the controls will involve theoretical evaluation of design, simulated checks of potential controls and factory and industry experience involving observations. Theoretical evidence and other information sources are used as a basis for validating effective design of controls with the PRP or HACCP Plan.

Level 1.**Industrial practice**
Level 2.**Theoretical Analysis**
Level 3.**Predictive Techniques**
Level 4.**Plant Trials**

Procedure
This procedure will analyse the effectiveness of a given control measure using a standard trial approach.

a) State the Hazard

b) Detail the control measure to be tested

c) State the objective of the trial

d) Record the no. of samples

e) State when the samples will be taken

f) State who is responsible for managing, conducting and reporting the trial.

g) Record the performance criteria

h) Record any support material

Records

VAL001a Industrial Control
VAL001b Theoretical Control
VAL001c Modeling Log
VAL001d Trial log

Fig. 7.8 Example of Records within the Validation Manual

Scope - **Microbiological**				Responsible: **JH**			Factory Area: **Trimming**	

Hazard Survival of **organisms**

No. Samples / Observations: 5 samples take with observations via checklists & ATP

Process Step	Observations / Sample No.	Time Sample / Observation Taken & Description	Equipment Required	Performance Targets	Actual Results	Reference Material	Validated Target
Trimming	1 5 samples and prep agar plates	1700 - 10cm area taken with 5 swabs	Incubator	No gross debris Condition of contact surface at end of production	1,000,000 CFUs ATP 20,000 RLUs	Hygiene management system Microbial Data	ATP <200RLUs CFU <200/100cm²
Trimming	2 5 samples and prep agar plates	1715 - surface has been rinsed	Incubator	Removal of surface soil and debris from contact surface	10,000 CFUs ATP 1000 RLUs	Hygiene management system Microbial Data	ATP <200RLUs CFU <200/100cm²
Trimming	3 5 samples and prep agar plates	1745 - surface has been clean and sanitised	Incubator	Removal of surface soil and contaminants look visibly clean. No chemical residue and damp surface	100 CFUs ATP 150 RLUs	Hygiene management system Microbial Data	ATP <200RLUs CFU <200/100cm²
Trimming	4			No surface	100 CF		

Validation Reference Material Sources		VAL001a		Area Risk: **High**
				Source: **Personnel**

Process Step: **Trimming**   Hazard Cleaning & Sanitation   Factory Area: **Trimming**

Control Measures: **Prevention of growth of Microflora**   Current Target / Tolerance Limit: 50 cfu / ml (200 RLU)

Information Source	Reference Material (Title/Year Volume/Pages)	Reference Source (Paper/Article)	Recommended Target Limit/ Tolerance	Are Data/ methods applicable to the product?		Current Limits Acceptable		Further Validation Required		If yes, state reason for not validating	If no, state reason for not validating
				Yes	No	Yes	No	Yes	No		
Trade association IFST / GMP	ATP levels in Diary Ind Vol 33 (1998) 55 - 76	IFST Journal	30 cfu/ml 250 RLUs		N				N		Currently within current Standards
Trade reference material Journals, Magazines	Vol. 9 No. 3 (1998) 11	Int. Food Hygiene	60 cfu/ml 250 RLUs	Y		Y			N		Currently Within Recommended Data set
Legislative Material											

The company has now:

- surveyed plant and noted problems

- decided an appropriate cleaning plan

- practically operated and modified the plan

- documented any evidence to prove it works and, if necessary, commissioned trials in high risk areas.

This chapter shall be reviewed in conjunction with Chapter 6, which discusses practical methods which may be employed within validation.

Chapter 8. SOFTWARE SUPPORT TOOLS FOR MANAGEMENT

8.1 Background

The last decade has seen the arrival of the electronic age to all business sectors including food. President Clinton has predicted that 40% of trade will be undertaken electronically by the middle of the next century. The massive expansion of global communication will mean that any business will be required to quickly demonstrate that it is in compliance with an existing customer or legislative standard or can move quickly to meet customer needs. This chapter will describe software tools which can put the food management team in control of the cleaning process.

8.2 Managing Information

In work recently reported the failure rate of HACCP plans caused by poor cleaning was given as 40%. The authors' own research has demonstrated that many cleaning plans are informal, poorly documented with little available evidence to prove the system is valid or confirmation that it continues to work. The work has also shown that in some instances, including high risk areas, microbial counts after cleaning may be higher than before cleaning. A variety of research projects led to the development of a series of software tools which are capable of managing hygiene or cleaning systems. Figure 8.1 provides an overview of a specific software tool designed to document, cost, validate and monitor cleaning plans which can illustrate the benefits of a software approach .

Fig. 8.1 Overview of Cost-it

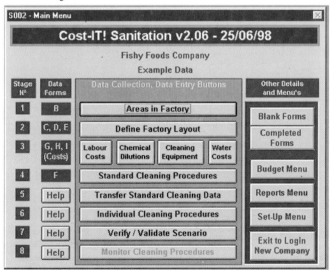

8.2.1 Software Tools

This software support tool will assist the manager to build, validate and manage their cleaning programme through a logical eight step process. The left hand side of the screen lists the data forms which can be produced to guide the manager and the right hand side gives the key output reports which may be required. The first three stages listed on the central screen capture the background information from the company which allows generic costing and analysis per area or item to be computed. Step 4 allows standard cleaning procedures to be generated quickly and step 5 enables these procedures to be transformed and scaled through the factory. Unique cleaning procedures may be logged in step 6 and finally the effectiveness of the programme validated through a structured process. When these steps are completed and the effectiveness of the programme validated, routine monitoring may take place to ensure that the cleaning programme is in control. We can see then that IT tools can be useful management of information

Fig. 8.2 The Main Benefits of Software Tools for Cleaning

8.2.2 Setting up a Cleaning Plan

The software guides the user through the set up and validation of the cleaning plan. This provides the manager with a systematic approach to building a cleaning procedure - the key steps can be edited through drop down boxes. The procedures are therefore quick to enter and easy to edit.

Fig. 8.3 Software Tool - Cleaning Method

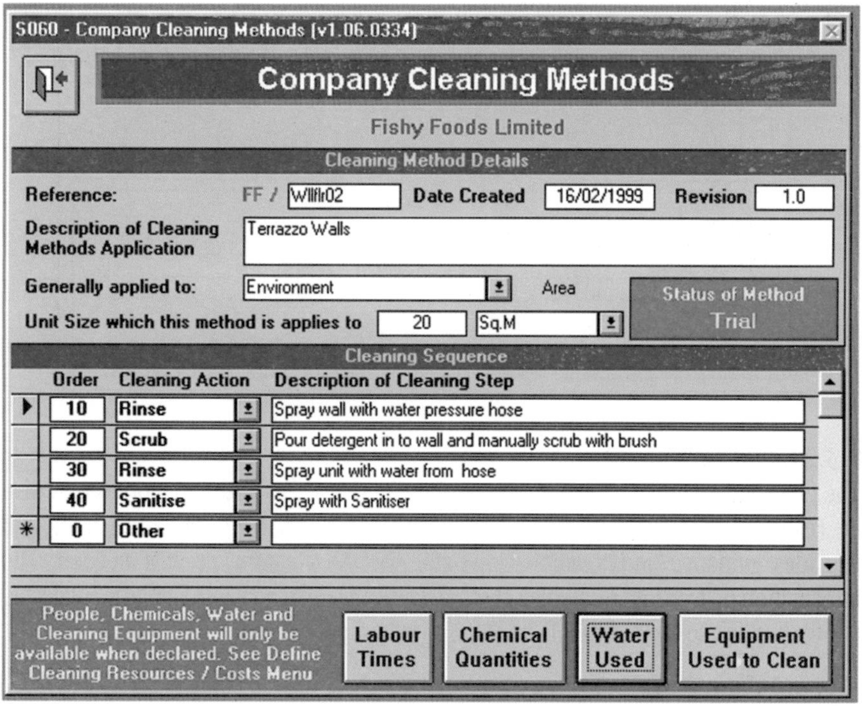

The drop down boxes for labour times, chemical quantities, water usage and equipment used to clean are shown figures 8.4/8.5/8.6/8.7

8.3 Defining Cleaning Resources

8.3.1 Labour

The user can allocate specific labour types and time to enable detailed labour costing if desired. Labour types may vary from specific cleaning staff to production team. The analysis of labour utilisation highlights to the company the use of expensive labour during cleaning e.g engineering time.

Fig. 8.4 Software Tool - Labour

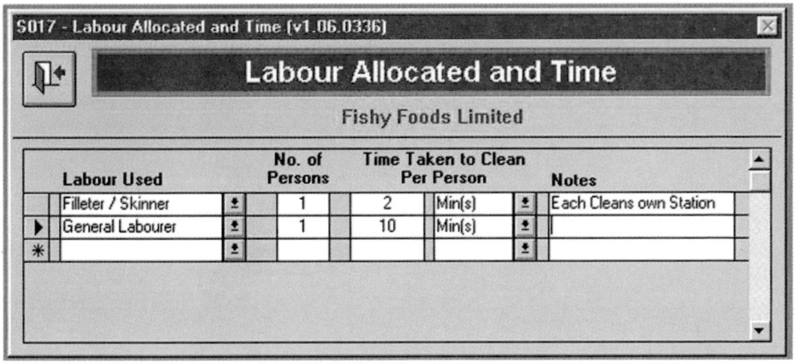

8.3.2 Chemical Quantities

The chemical action, type used, estimated quantity and any additional notes may also be recorded. The dilution method used is also linked to the chemical table and provides guidance and a quick calculator for the cleaning crew if needed. The information on type and quantities of chemicals is useful when any change is suggested allowing quick cost assessment and re-issue of new procedures.

Fig. 8.5 Chemicals

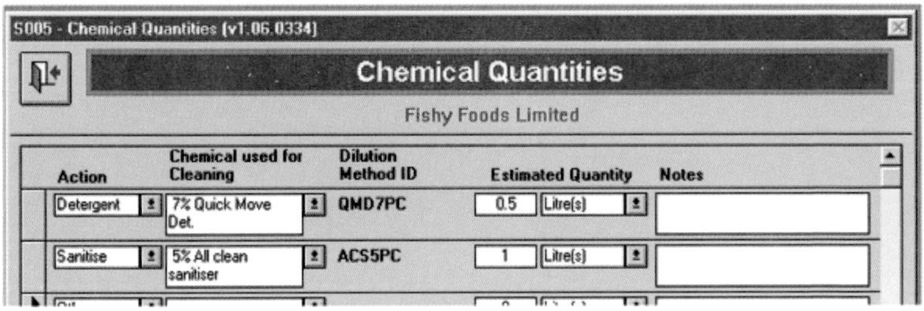

8.4 Recording Test Data

The software provides a simple approach for the manager to follow when validating - i.e proving that the system works. In the early version of the software this involved visual inspection, ATP and final microbial checks for specific surfaces. The guidance provided in Chapter 6 will enable the manager and the team to select which assessment approach is best. Chapter 7 also gives guidance on demonstrating the industrial practice, theoretical justification and any factory trials. All of this test data may be entered to support the case that the business was being "duly diligent".

Fig. 8.6 Validation Log

Area	Item(s) for Cleaning	Method Ref	Method Description	Status
Reception area	chute	FF \ Chute01	Conveyors/Belts/Chutes (Length)	Active
Packing area	floors	FF \ WllFlr01	Wall - Taken from the Process area wall of 7.2m x 2m	Active
Packing area	walls	FF \ WllFlr01	Wall - Taken from the Process area wall of 7.2m x 2m	Active
Packing area	Stainless steel tables	FF \ SST01	Stainless steel table, general worker surfaces	Active
Process and Trimming	floors	FF \ WllFlr01	Wall - Taken from the Process area wall of 7.2m x 2m	Active
Process and Trimming	walls	FF \ WllFlr01	Wall - Taken from the Process area wall of 7.2m x 2m	Active
Process and Trimming	small worktable	FF \ SST01	Stainless steel table, general worker surfaces	Active
Process and Trimming	Stainless steel tables	FF \ SST01	Stainless steel table, general worker surfaces	Active

Test	Date	Result	Units	When Taken	Evaluation	Notes
Visual	27/03/1999	7	out of 10	After Sanitising	Pass	Production Staff Recleaned (7am)
Visual	27/03/1999	4	out of 10	After Sanitising	Fail	3 Staff Sick (6am) Cleaning Limited
Visual	26/02/1999		out of 10	After Sanitising	Pass	
Visual						

The manager may focus on analysing the performance of an area and therefore review the costs and monitor trends. Any changes to standard cleaning procedures may be undertaken for the whole factory and the modified documentation re-issued electronically or by hard copy. The manager may ask for key monitoring data to be provided and electronically "verify" that the area is in control.

The next section of the chapter will discuss the importance of costing and review the software tools used to calculate cost impact of change. This will be reviewed in a four step approach.

8.5 Step 1 - Documenting Existing Systems

The software produces a series of checklists to guide the manager through documenting the existing controls. The survey sheets are entered into the computer and the programme produces standard cleaning procedures, records and schedules.

8.5.1 Water Utilisation

The water type, quantity and temperature may be recorded per method or per area. Water and effluent costs are continually rising and must become a subject of increasing management focus.

Fig. 8.7 Water Utilisation

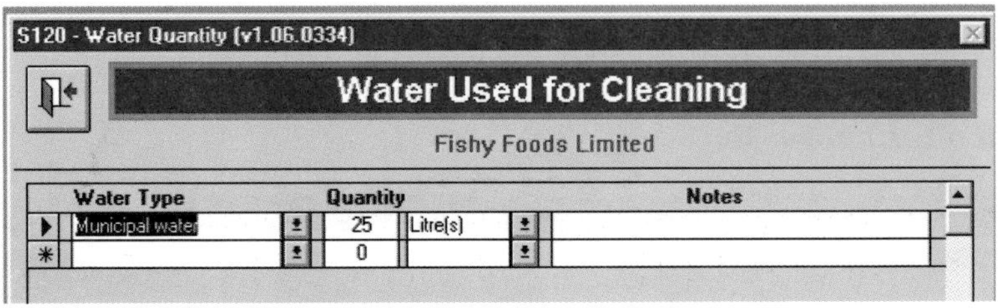

S120 - Water Quantity (v1.06.0334)							☒
Water Used for Cleaning							
Fishy Foods Limited							
	Water Type		**Quantity**			**Notes**	
▶	Municipal water	±	25	Litre(s)	±		
*		±	0		±		

8.5.2 Equipment Used for Cleaning

Traceability of items of small equipment is made easier by logging their use per method and by area. This may be linked to a colour coding system to prevent cross contamination in high care facilities. Additionally the use of cloths, brushes and scrubbers must be monitored closely as they have been shown as common vectors of contamination. The replacement time of units may be assessed or even fixed using software. Response to regular visual or other checks can be logged in the software.

Fig. 8.8 Cleaning Equipment

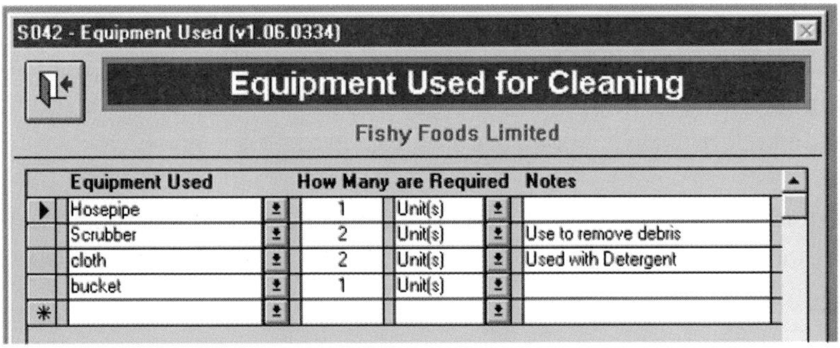

S042 - Equipment Used (v1.06.0334)							☒
Equipment Used for Cleaning							
Fishy Foods Limited							
	Equipment Used		**How Many are Required**			**Notes**	
▶	Hosepipe	±	1	Unit(s)	±		
	Scrubber	±	2	Unit(s)	±	Use to remove debris	
	cloth	±	2	Unit(s)	±	Used with Detergent	
	bucket	±	1	Unit(s)	±		
*		±			±		

Fig. 8.9 Example of Survey Tool

FORM F Cleaning Procedures for Standard Items		*Printed On: 17/03/98 17:01:44*
		Page 1

Company: _____   **Scenario:** _____

Standardised Desc (see seperate list) _____

No of Units: _____	Unit size _____	SqFt (Area)	Gal.(s) (Volume)

Status: (Circle as required)

When cleaned:	*DURING* Production
	OUTSIDE Production

How many Times is the item cleaned

Once, Twice, Three, Four	every	Hour, Day, Shift, Week, Year, Tonne, Intake

Condition *New, Satisfactory, Poor*

Soiling: *Light, Medium, Heavy*

Step No	Action No	Labour	Application o	Chemical (Actions 3 and 4 only)
1		No of persons Time spent in Minutes Labour	Equipment Amount	Dilution as % or ppm. Name
2		No of persons Time spent in Minutes Labour	Equipment Amount	Dilution as % or ppm. Name
3		No of persons Time spent in Minutes Labour	Equipment Amount	Dilution as % or ppm. Name
4		No of persons Time spent in Minutes Labour	Equipment Amount	Dilution as % or ppm. Name
5		No of persons Time spent in Minutes Labour	Equipment Amount	Dilution as % or ppm. Name
6		No of persons Time spent in Minutes Labour	Equipment Amount	Dilution as % or ppm. Name
		No of persons t in Minutes	Equipment	Dilution as % or ppm.

The manager should log the sequence of cleaning, gather any existing documentation and record typical actions when failure occur. The software package produces the checklists to guide the team, highlights if any key data has not been collected and finally produces the appropriate cleaning manuals as required. After this has been entered the company will have a flexible documented cleaning management system.

Fig 8.10 Example of Reports

Cleaning Method/Procedure

Method Ref: FF\Wllflr02   **Date Created**: 16/02/99   **Revision**: 1.0
Description: Terrazzo Walls
Applies to: 20Sq.M   **Environment**

Sequence	Action	Description
10	Rinse	Spray wall with water pressure hose
20	Scrub	Pour detergent in to wall and manually scrub
30	Rinse	Spray unit with water from hose
40	Sanitise	Spray with sanitiser

Equipment Required

Equipment used for Cleaning	Number Required
Hosepipe	1 unit
Scrubber	1 un
Cloth	2 u
Bucket	1

Labour Requ

Responsibilty for Cleaning

General labourer

Filleter / Skinner

Chemical

Chemical and Dilution

7% Quick Move Dept.

5% All clean sanitiser

Wat

Water Used

Municipal Water

Fishy Foods Ltd. - Cleaning Schedule

Scenario: BMARK - Bench Mark
Factory Area: Reception area

Item Description	Frequency	Cleaning Method
chute	2 per Wk	FF\Chute01
small worktable	1 per Day	FF\SST01
Tubs for washed fish	1 per WK	FF\Ftub01
walls	1 per Wk	FF\WllFlr01
floors	1 per Day	FF\WllFlr01
Stainless Steel tables	1 per Day	FF\SST01

Factory Area: Process and Trimming area

Item Description	Frequency	Cleaning Method
Stainless Steel tables	1 per Day	FF\SST01
small worktable	1 per Day	FF\SST01
walls	1 per Wk	FF\WllFlr01
floors	1 per Day	FF\WllFlr01

Factory area: Packing area

Item Description	Frequency	Cleaning Method
floors	1 per Day	FF\WllFlr01
walls	1 per Day	FF\WllFlr01
Stainless Steel tables	1 per Day	FF\SST01

8.5.3 Step 2 - Costing Existing Systems

Costs for existing cleaning are collected and expressed as % of total spend which provides an overview of the total cost to operate the cleanup within the factories or selected areas. This reveals were the majority of money is being spent and enables the manager to improve the use of resources before proceeding with any investment decisions, see chapter 5 fig. 5.2.

The typical cost profile for cleaning within a company primarily involves labour. The saving that the company can make on chemicals in a developed country may therefore be minimal and the benefits of organisation and training are therefore high if marginal cost of labour can be reduced. The increasing cost of effluent control within the UK factories may see a 10 to 20 fold increase within the next 2 years and a focus on effective cleaning to minimise both the strength and volume of effluent will be increasingly important.

8.5.4 Cleaning Costs

Table 8.1 provides a costed option for the cleaning of the *Fishy Foods* and includes both direct costs and indirect costs, the latter often being overlooked. The user may use the software tool to analyse and allocate costs to a given cost centre (factory areas). This is routinely done in the plant when budgets and variance targets are agreed based on an "apportioned" allocation of cost to a given production area. Table 8.1 shows how the manager and the team can review their current performance. A series of costing definitions will be provided for the reader in the appendix. However we will often be discussing direct and indirect costs. A direct cost is one which is related to a specific product whereas indirect costs cannot be linked. Examples of direct costs are raw materials, directly attributable labour. Examples of indirect costs include factory rent, management wages, interest on loans etc .

Table 8.1 - Cost of Cleaning Summary Printout

Cost of Cleaning per Year	Printed On: 01/06/1999 12:34:12			Page 1
Company: Fishy Foods Company		**Scenario:** *Process Area 1*		

Description	Quantity	Unit Cost	Cost (£)	Percentage of total
Direct Cost - Labour				
Unskilled Hygiene	545.3 Hour(s)	10.00	5,453.43	64.7%
Unskilled Labourer	80.0 Hour(s)	8.00	640.00	7.6%
		Labour Total	**6,093.43**	**72.3%**
Direct Cost - Materials				
Hydrochlorite	0.9 Gal.(s)	8.50	7.24	0.1%
Isbest Cleaner	40.8 Gal.(s)	15.00	612.55	7.3%
SnowWhiter	297.4 Gal.(s)	2.49	740.48	8.8%
		Materials Total	**1,360.27**	**16.1%**
Direct Cost - Water				
Bore Hole water	27,859.7 Gal.(s)	0.00	27.86	0.3%
		Water Total	**27.86**	**0.3%**

| **Indirect Costs** | | | | | |
Description	Quantity	Unit cost	Total cost	Basis of App. 10%	Apportioned cost
Management time	500	£20	£10000	10%	£1000
Foam Applicator	2	£2500	£5000	10%	£1000
Pressure washer	2	£1000	£2000	10%	£200
Small items	50	£20	£1000	10%	£100

Management may wish to measure costs directly attributable to a process area - we can see that labour, materials and water are itemised. The indirect costs of cleaning e.g. management time and equipment have been allocated on a basis of 10% to this process area.

The example provided is based on data from the East Coast of Canada. The reader should note that water is free, effluent cost are absent and units of measurement are in gallons.

8.5.5 Step 3 - Measuring Effectiveness

The manager now checks that the control measures work using accepted microbial tests and rapid methods. A validation protocol was designed and was operated to check the effectiveness of the selected cleaning procedures. The protocol is included within the software package and the costing exercise is not finished until this has been entered. These checks ensure that company money is being well spent.

Table 8.2 ATP Pass/Fails from Selected Categories in 6 Factories Visited.

Category	Total Samples	Failures	Percentage
Environment	38	12	32%
Equipment	47	26	55%
Food Contacts	69	27	39%
Vector	23	18	78%

We can see that the initial ATP failure rate from the plants indicated that cleaning equipment (vectors) often failed. Target values are normally set by testing the appropriate surface after cleaning or may be provided by the equipment manufacturer. If the results are above the limit then the company must re-clean and retest before "validating" the protocol. The inability to reach a given level may be the result of poor cleaning method, inappropriate chemicals or use of chemicals, poor surface or even that the testing unit is faulty. Assuming the instrument is calibrated properly, then an investigation as to why cleaning is not effective under the other headings - method, materials, or equipment must be undertaken.

8.5.6 Benchmarking

Internal benchmarking can be defined as: "comparison of similar operations or functions across a company, or with associated companies, in order or identify the level of service (control) that is best practice within this common operation".

Benchmarking is recognised as being an essential component of any continuous improvement process and involves the measurement of specified elements of product, services or practices against a selected reference point- e.g internal best practice ,best competition or industry standard. The rapidly changing food sector demands approaches which enable the business to maintain or exceed established benchmarks if they are to succeed.

Many current food safety programmes have attempted to retrospectively measure the effectiveness and costs of their food safety programme after making changes. "Benchmarking" techniques are therefore recommended to analyse the food safety systems prior to change. Food safety systems are composed of a series of integrated control measures- including cleaning programmes. The previous software tools described were initally used in the benchmarking of cleaning programmes including recording data on effectiveness and producing documented manuals, procedures and records for typical management control prior to change. The records may then be used as a reference point for routine monitoring and improvement cycles.

8.5.7 Benchmarking Cleaning

A software benchmarking package has now been developed which captures key information, analyses defect types and scores the company performance against an agreed reference standard directing "continuous improvement" within the business.

The benchmarks suggested included markers for management and cleaning effectiveness and are summarised in Fig 8.11. The manager may use the "benchmarks" to guide the improvement program.

Fig. 8.11 - Example Benchmarks for Effective Sanitation

Standard - SANITATION BENCHMARKING		
Elements	**Scoring Scheme**	
Cleaning plan/ Documentation Management awareness /understanding Management Control Corrective Action Operational compliance Cost control	<u>Score</u> <u>Description</u> 0 No evidence 25 Some Evidence 50 No defined approach 75 Defined Approach 100 Benchmark standard	<u>Compliance category</u> Critical Major Minor Pass Pass

8.5.8 Step 4 - Improving Control - Low Cost /No Cost

The manager should assess the operational control and understanding within the existing cleaning plan. These "benchmarks" of effective cleaning have been built into a new software tool specificaly designed for benchmarking.

Examples of Decisions to Improve - Low Cost/No Cost

The software may be used to calculate the "predicted cost" of a given change while making sure the new control is more or similarly effective. Changes which have been observed include.

1 - Change in Chemical - Detergents and Sanitisers

The existing clean was often ineffective because the "detergent" was too dilute to effectively lift the dirt from the surface. The management and crew reviewed the effect of increasing the detergent concentration balanced with a 33% reduction in labour effort resulting in an effective clean with a cost saving.

2 - Sanitiser/Disinfectant

Observations and objective tests of cleaning indicated the disinfectants were often ineffective. On investigation the contact time or residual organic load was minimising the killing effort of the chemical. The assurance that the initial phase of cleaning was working resulted in effective disinfection at no increased cost to plants.

3 - Changes in Labour Utilisation- Training

The cleaning crew had often received no formal support causing many of the "vectors " they used to be contaminated. After initial visits and on the job training the increased "awareness and understanding" resulted in effective cleaning as proper care of cleaning equipment and materials took place combined with an understanding of how to clean. Typical training costs were low and easily recovered through improved cleaning e.g. £500 / day for 10 cleaning crew on site and similarly £500 for supervisor to attend more detailed off site training.

4 - Plant Surfaces

The condition of food contact surfaces e.g. preparation boards or belts, often made cleaning difficult. Some factories changed the boards, others arranged to have the surface skimmed to present a new less pitted surface. The board example cost the factory a few hundred pounds. The software tools enabled improvements to be justified, documented and managed and has often been achieved using the existing facilities with little investment. The use of software in supporting investment decisions will now be reviewed.

8.6 Software Tools for Investment Support

The factory may find that some of the equipment or infrastructure will require upgrading to meet a standard or new production demands. In that instance the four step process described has provided much of the key information necessary for the investment proposal.

8.6.1 Investment Proposal - Improving Cleaning in Place (CIP) Systems

The initial cleaning software tools have focused on managing direct and indirect costs within relatively simple cleaning plans. A recent innovation has been the development of an investment decision making tool for companies investing in a new Biotrace ATP monitoring and control system. This software will enable the manager of a plant to decide whether the investment in a new piece of cleaning control equipment is justified for cleaning in place (CIP) systems. This type of cleaning requires a large quantity of water and chemicals and better control of effective cleaning may result in significant savings by the business.

The software system is designed to guide the manager through the cost/ benefit analysis of this investment and will allow the company to insert a range of key variables and "cost"" the impact.

Fig. 8.12 Cost Benefit Scenario

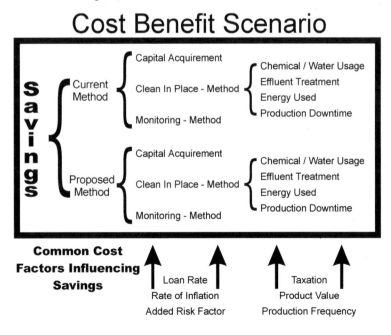

The factory financial team will wish to enter the risk factors for the capital and will set an acceptable rate of return for the capital employed. This information allows the cost case being made by the technical team to be understood and evaluated by finance.

Fig. 8.13 Screen which Enables Comparison of New and Old CIP Cycles

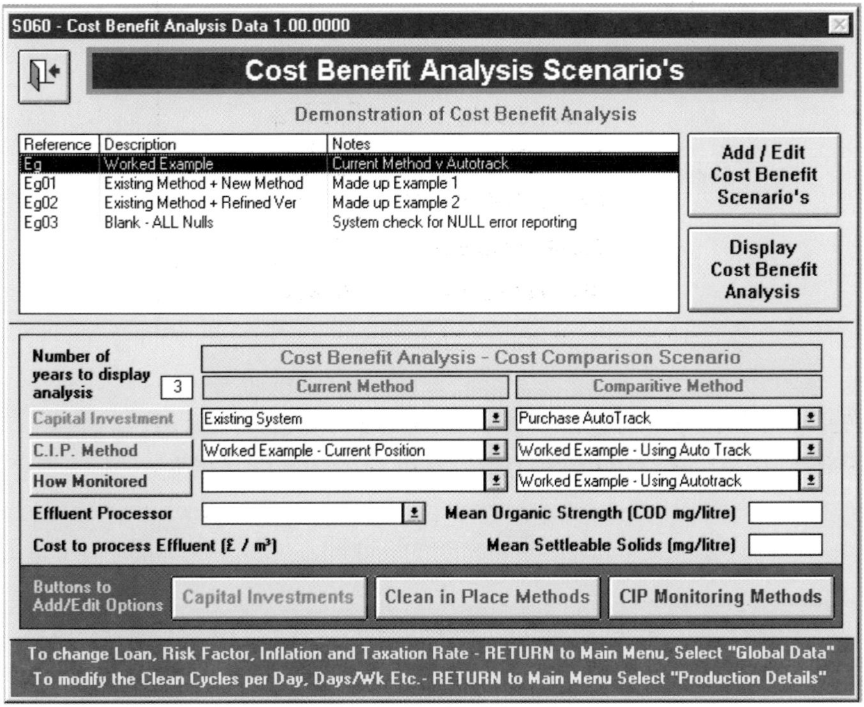

The software will allow a detailed analysis of the cost of effluent production before and after the purchase of the new control system.

Fig. 8.14 Screens enabling the manager to enter the financial factors to be examined in the cost benefit analysis.

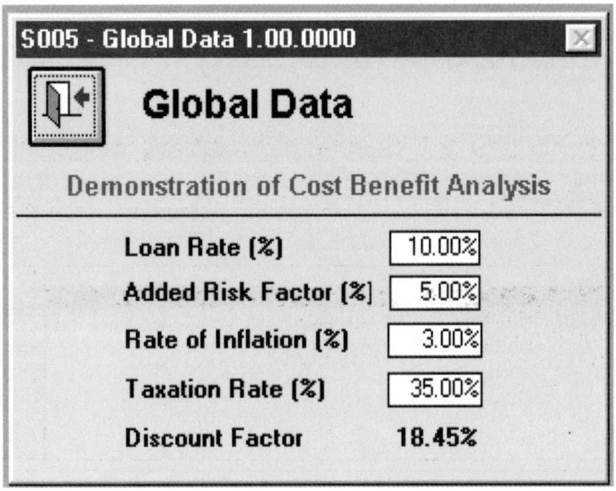

Fig. 8.15 Example outputs - providing a quick overview of assumptions, key financial ratios and expected payback.

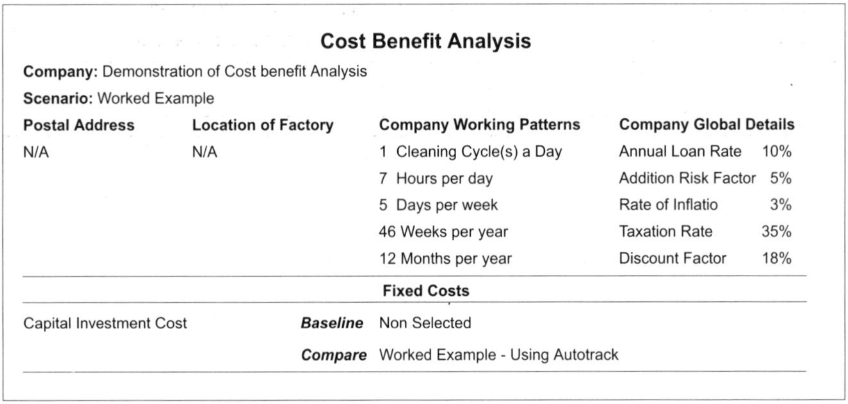

Cost Benefit Analysis

Company: Demonstration of Cost benefit Analysis

Scenario: Worked Example

Postal Address	Location of Factory	Company Working Patterns	Company Global Details	
N/A	N/A	1 Cleaning Cycle(s) a Day	Annual Loan Rate	10%
		7 Hours per day	Addition Risk Factor	5%
		5 Days per week	Rate of Inflatio	3%
		46 Weeks per year	Taxation Rate	35%
		12 Months per year	Discount Factor	18%

Fixed Costs		
Capital Investment Cost	*Baseline*	Non Selected
	Compare	Worked Example - Using Autotrack

8.7 Cost analysis

A series of costing description will be provided for the reader in Appendix 5. However we will often be discussing direct and indirect costs which are a means of classifying costs commonly used in industry. A direct cost is one which is related to a specific product whereas indirect costs cannot be linked. Examples of direct costs are raw materials, directly attributable labour or commission paid to someone for selling a specific product. Examples of indirect costs include factory rent, management wages, interest on loans etc.

8.7.1 Investment software

This software tool forms a bridge between cost of cleaning and waste (or effluent) minimisation. Senior management can now analyse this data in a realistic way using selected financial ratios and come to a decision based on accurate data. The "technical team" has communicated effectively to the senior management and made a good case for investment. The company can now decide whether the investment borrowed at an interest rate of a given percentage is acceptable. Previous data on the existing cleaning control and its effectiveness can be used to justify the expenditure.

Current developments within the UK are targeting the further refinement of this simple CAPEX tools (capital expenditure) tool which enables senior management to screen the costing using selected financial ratios and to perform given sensitivity analysis e.g. effect of inflation, increase in water charge, effluent costs before committing money.

The costs and benefits are systematically and flexibly analysed and a historical record of the cost projections, benefits and sensitivity analysis will also be held in the output report and on computer file. This can then be tracked through the plant trials and ongoing operation of the cleaning system.

8.8 Off the Shelf Software

The previous discussion focused on research and customised software. Innovise Software produce several off the shelf packages used in generic cleaning which are raising interest in the food sector. Estimator is a Computerised Resource Estimating and Costing tool. It uses standard productivity rates, combined with local variables to calculate the time required to carry out user defined tasks. The information generated can be used to produce quotes or further analysed to assess distribution of labour and calculate additional resources which may be required to carry out operations. There is also a "what if" facility to allow analysis of possible situations. Other packages include Comtrac - Computer Aided Cleaning Management which uses bar codes to optimise the time of staff and to monitor quality of service delivered. StockWATCH   which is a tool to control stocks of materials and enable automatic ordering, which again uses bar coding. AssetTrac can be used to manage equipment, assets and maintenance using tagging.

8.9 Make a Plan
A good plan should assist the management in achieving cost effective control because:

- Allocation of budgets and performance targets to team enables:
  measurement of performance

- Prevents unnecessary damage to capital equipment by:
  defining cleaning procedures
  selecting correct chemicals
  ensuring equipment is cleanable prior to purchase

- Minimises downtime:
  prevents electrical equipment being shorted through proper training and
  procedures
  ensures correct reassembly prior to start up
  planned clean at product changeover ensuring minimal time

- Ensures process efficiency:
  reduces build of scale or biofilm formation therefore ensuring optimal heat
  transfer

The ability to cost an existing cleaning plan, predict the cost of a newer modified plan provides management with a useful budgeting and monitoring tool. The software system described in section 8.1 also captures and manages cost data (hence the name!).

Key outputs include:

- Costed cleaning programme
- Budgets
- Cost scenarios

8.10 Consider the Investment
Traditionally business has viewed expenditure related to meeting cleaning standards as avoidable where possible and a necessary evil when forced to make the change. Few of

the small to medium sized enterprises have made their investment decisions formally and the systematic collection of operational cost data required by this software provides a basis for investment decision . The decision to "invest" in an improvement to meet a market standards will require realistic cost and business efficiency data to calculate expected returns. The costing tool will help prepare reliable cost data which the financial team may analyse quickly using the investment software.

Increasing pressure has been placed on businesses to implement better control systems but without a balanced economic appraisal, the system may not progress.

Additionally the success of the implementation of a new cleaning system is dependent on the attitude of the team as well as a financial commitment. Money made available under threat is often not accompanied by the drive from senior management for success based on a shared vision.

8.11 Checking the Cleaning Systems

Food safety systems are composed of two main component areas - critical control activities and their supporting pre-requisite programmes. The weaknesses in a given system can be identified by the use of a formal audit tool followed by costing the options to achieve a given improvement. One of the major failings in investment proposals has been the lack of focus on measuring the effectiveness of existing and new controls . The software tool will assist the manager in preparing a proposal by providing a range of cost based reports on existing or new scenarios. The software tool will guide management through a systematic costing of cleaning by :-

- documenting the current cleaning control of the plants

- costing this cleaning systems

- measuring the effectiveness

- costing and implementing necessary improvements.

If the control system still failed to meet market or legal standards or an opportunity existed to significantly improve control on an economic basis then this four step approach was used to prepare investment proposal options.

8.12 Summary and Conclusions

The first section emphasised the benefits of control of information in the form of documents, procedures, records and overall cleaning plans. The second section discussed the role of IT support tools in managing and controlling the cost of resources.

Fig. 8.17 Targets set to achieve effective control

Cost effective control software may be used to measure and analyse direct, indirect and capital expenditure costs. Attention has been increasingly given to the cost associated with lost sales, product recall and legal liability suits resulting from failure to properly clean. Senior managers are often asked to make decisions on technical improvements to the factories with little justification or alternative options available. The technical manager must make a case for improvement to win the commitment of the directorate. The success of the implementation of a new cleaning system is dependent on the attitude of the senior management team as well as financial commitment.

Investment options to improve these systems should be systematically assessed and selected improvements to controls should then be implemented. The performance measures for the improved controls should be established after the targets have been agreed and set with workforce and relevant management team. Routine monitoring of targets and of payback should be put in place.

All of this is much easier when supported by dedicated software tools !!

Chapter 9. CLEANING IN CATERING / FOOD SERVICE OPERATIONS

9.1 Background

Hygiene, cleaning and disinfection (sanitation and sanitising) in catering (food service) establishments share many similarities to food manufacturing but have specific differences and problems. A key feature is that catering establishments SERVE food as well as prepare it. This means that in addition to all the food preparation utensils and premises, the crockery / cutlery for food service also need cleaning. Both the premises and the crockery /cutlery are seen by the consumer who may use observable standards of cleanliness as a means of judging the business. Dirty crockery / cutlery can present a bad image and lose customers. The extent of any problems will depend upon the size and type of catering operation (see Fig 9.1). Differences between catering and food manufacturing are summarised in Table 9.1 although these differences are less for larger catering operations.

Overall, the net effect of these differences is to make cleaning more difficult (see Table 9.2). Other than the aesthetic perspective and customer opinion the importance of cleaning in catering establishments should not be underestimated. This importance is emphasised by recent data which implicates catering operations as the major location for general outbreaks of food poisoning with cross contamination as a risk factor in 39% of outbreaks. Cross contamination (and thus unclean utensils / surfaces) may be of particular importance in catering operations as food is frequently prepared well in advance of consumption. Such pre-prepared food must be handled correctly, using clean equipment / surfaces, so that once prepared the food is not re-contaminated prior to consumption.

The potential for unclean surfaces to cause cross contamination and result in food poisoning is of particular concern with *Campylobacter*, *Escherichia coli* 0157 and small round structured viruses (SRSV) as these pathogens have a very low minimum infective dose i.e. contamination of food on its own can cause illness rather than, as required for *Salmonella*, contamination plus growth. Microbiological studies of catering kitchens have revealed the presence of a wide range of food pathogens in a variety of kitchen locations (see Table 9.3). The need for keeping cleaning equipment clean is illustrated by the presence of pathogens associated with dish / wiping cloths.

Fig. 9.1 Type and Size of Catering Operations and Food Safety Systems

SMALL ⟶ **MEDIUM** ⟶ **LARGE**

e.g.   e.g.   e.g.
Guesthouse   Restaurant   In-flight catering

ASC/SAFE ⟵⟶ **HACCP**

ASC   - Assured Safe Catering
SAFE   - Systematic Assessment of Food Environment
HACCP - Hazard Analysis Critical Control Point

Table 9.1 Difference Between Catering and Food Manufacturing Operation

CATERING	FOOD MANUFACTURE
Produce and serve	Produce only
Production in peaks and troughs	Even production
Usually whole meals	Often single food items only
Little scientific support	Good scientific support
Ill defined product	Well defined product
Little or informal Quality Assurance (QA)	Formal comprehensive QA
Wider product range smaller scale	Limited product range larger scale
Little research and development	Considerable research and development
Small scale equipment	Large scale equipment

Table 9.2 Factors Affecting Cleaning / Disinfecting in Catering Operations

FACTOR	IMPLICATIONS / CONSEQUENCES
Staff	Typically large numbers of low paid part - time staff often with poor educational background. Staff turnover may be high and all these factors impact upon training, motivation etc.
Produce and Serve	Large numbers of additional small items (trays, tables, plates, cutlery) as well as food preparation utensils, require cleaning.
Preparation in peaks and troughs	Often high demand for clean equipment in short time spans. Food often prepared in advance needs to be handled / stored in clean conditions.
Little scientific support	Level of technical support much less in catering operations. Much less scientific evaluation / validation /monitoring of cleaning.
Wide product range	Cooked and uncooked products served. More difficulty in separating raw from cooked. "Clean as you go" especially important. Wider range of raw materials from many sources in food preparation areas brings in a variety of food soils and microorganisms.
Little or informal QA	Catering in general has less well developed and implemented cleaning programmes.
Small scale equipment	Few opportunities for CIP, equipment often more difficult to take apart and clean. More items need cleaning
Size of business	Catering industry is dominated by small businesses, often owner managed. Poor understanding of legislation and technical information by small businesses. Less time and money to invest in cleaning, often small and cramped food preparation areas, less well designed and constructed.

Table 9.3
Reported Isolations of Different Potential Pathogens From Specific Environmental Sites within Kitchens

Environmental Site	Campylobacter spp.	Salmonella spp.	Y. enterocolitica	S. aureus	E. coli	Bacillus spp.	B. cereus	L. monocytogenes
Dish Cloth				●	●	●		●
Cleaning Cloth		●		●			●	
Wash-up Sponge		●		●				●
Wash-up Brush					●			●
Wash Cloth		●						
Floor Mop					●	●		
Tea / Hand Towel				●	●	●		
Sink		●	●		●		●	●
Taps				●	●		●	
Refrigerator / Door				●	●		●	●
Waste / Pedal Bin				●	●	●		
Chopping Boards		●		●	●			●
Work Surfaces	●				●	●		
Floor	●				●			

9.2 Cleaning Premises

Cleaning of catering premises is often more difficult than in food manufacturing plants because they are less well designed and constructed. Often catering premises are in old buildings, ones designed for other purposes or even mobile. Constructional finishes are less substantial / heavy duty and more likely to wear out / trap food soil. Drainage is often not as good as in food manufacturing units. All the principles of cleaning / disinfection mentioned in the book apply but need to be implemented carefully in the catering context.

9.3 Cleaning Foods

Caterers may need to wash / clean a variety of foods especially "ready to eat" prior to service. This applies to all fresh fruit and vegetables to ensure removal of dirt, pests, chemicals and some removal of microorganisms. There is a world wide trade in fruit and vegetables, and there may be concerns about microbial contamination and hygiene standards in some countries. A number of large scale outbreaks of food poisoning have been associated with ready to eat fruit and vegetables imported from countries with lower hygiene standards. However, unnecessary cleaning of foods in catering establishments should be avoided as it can increase the chances of cross contamination. Washing the body cavity of poultry, widely practised in catering operations, has been found to contaminate the sink environment. It is debatable whether it reduces contamination of the inside of poultry. The inside of the bird is not eaten and stuffing the body cavity is a practice not to be encouraged as it increases cooking times.

Washing fruit and vegetables starts with good quality (potable) tap water but the effect is improved if a biocide is added. This can be chlorine based, e.g. sodium isocyanuric acid derivatives or alternatively ozonated water. The latter has the advantage of decomposing to leave oxygen and no other residues. Trials are also underway to investigate the continuous use of ozone in food display cabinets. The ability of ozone to deodorize as well as disinfect may be an added advantage e.g. in fish counters.

9.4 Cleaning Utensils

9.4.1 Separation of Utensils for Raw and Cooked Foods.

Utensils for raw foods must be kept separate from those for cooked foods and ideally washed in separate sinks / machines. This minimises the risk of cross contamination e.g. via tap handles. Colour coding of equipment, cloths, chopping boards, etc. helps to ensure that this separation is maintained.

Special care should be taken with dish cloths. Dirty dishes and sponges are bacterial reservoirs and are known for their cross contamination potential. Ideally disposable or disinfectant impregnated materials should be used. However antibacterial impregnated utensils are not a panacea, merely an aid. Actions resulting in cross contamination can occur frequently and rapidly long before impregnated chemicals have chance to kill off any contaminating bacteria. The use of antibacterial impregnated utensils/cloths can also lead to a false sense of security in staff using them. This is especially true as viruses are thought to be important in the majority of outbreaks where the contaminating organism is not identified.

9.4.2 Manual Cleaning of Equipment / Serving Utensils

Whether manual or automatic the same 5/6 cleaning stages apply. Automatic cycles in washing machines etc. guarantee more consistency of cleaning although not necessarily a better end result. An operative cleaning manually, unhappy with the results, can take immediate remedial action.

Single Sink System - In small establishments single sink systems are used, often in combination with a dishwasher (domestic or commercial standard). As much food debris as possible is removed from plates / utensils prior to immersion in a single sink containing hot water (50 - 60°C) and detergent. Ideally the water should be as hot as possible but operated below 60°C. At or above this temperature there is an increased risk of injury and caking / coagulation of food debris onto the plate.

Rubber gloves should be worn and the water will need frequent changing. If used for items in contact with raw foods, water from this sink should not be used to wet dish cloths prior to cleaning work surfaces. This latter practice, widely performed in catering, should not be encouraged especially for surfaces coming into contact with high risk foods.

Two / Three sink system - This is the preferred method for any businesses other than the smallest food operation. Crockery / utensils are prepared by scraping to remove food debris (into a suitable waste container) then rinsing with cold water. The first sink serves to clean, the second sink to disinfect and a third sink (if present) as a final rinse.

Step 1 — - Scrape off gross food debris, taking care with sticky items (jam, marmalade) and fatty deposits (cooked breakfasts) and then rinse in cold tap water.

Step 2 (sink 1) — - This is a cleaning stage using hot water (plus appropriate detergent) at 50-60°C. A brush should be used and gloves should be worn. The scraped crockery and utensils are washed in this sink, then removed and loaded into baskets / racks which are placed in sink 2.

Step 3	- This is a rinsing / disinfecting stage using water at 77 - 82°C.
(sink 2)	Baskets containing crockery are immersed for 1-2 minutes. This stage has three functions:-
(a)	to disinfect by heat any remaining bacteria;
(b)	to rinse off any remaining detergent;
(c)	after removal from this sink items should be hot enough to air dry so avoiding use of a tea towel which could cause re-contamination.

Care is required to prevent hands being scalded.

Washing up and rinsing water should be changed frequently and gloves, sinks, drainers and all other surfaces should also be cleaned. The approximate throughput for a manual system is 600 pieces per hour. The order of washing up must be carefully planned, e.g. lightly soiled articles such as glasses should be cleaned first. The process is slow, costly (labour intensive) and mechanical dishwashing may be preferable and often more economic. Cloth drying of washed items should be avoided and handling of items should be minimal to avoid re-contamination. Care should be taken not to re-contaminate the surfaces of washed items during storage or laying up of tables.

9.4.3 Dish Washing Machines

These can be used for washing crockery as well as preparation equipment including chopping boards. Wooden chopping boards (even hardwood) should not be put in a dish washer. One recent recommendation was that wooden chopping boards are best disinfected by putting in a microwave oven on full power for 5 minutes or more.

There are various types available depending on the size of the cleaning operation. These include:

(a)   single tank

(b)   multi-tank with racks on conveyor

(c)   multi-tank with conveyor belt (direct feed)

Excess food should be removed from all items before loading into the machines.

How to Clean

Single Tank machines involve hand loading / unloading of racks of tableware. The cleaning cycle is similar to manual washing up, i.e. detergent is sprayed onto items at 50-60°C followed by a hot water rinse (82°C). Usual throughput for this machine is equivalent to approximately 45 meals / hour.

Multi-tank machines have racks on conveyors, onto which the tableware is loaded prior to being placed on the conveyor belt. This gives a much higher throughput equivalent to approximately 250-300 meals/hour. This type of dishwasher has a pre-wash section, followed by a detergent spray, a power rinse at 70°C to remove detergent and a final hot water disinfecting rinse at 82°C.

In very large restaurants and many hospitals dishes are loaded directly onto a specially constructed conveyor belt directly feeding the multi-tank.

All machines should be serviced regularly and periodic checks made to ensure that all temperatures on the dials are an accurate record of actual water temperatures, the correct level of detergent is being added, spray jets are unblocked and reaching all parts of the machine whatever the loading patterns and the track speed is appropriate and consistant.

Washed items should be checked for correct cleaning. Any faults in dish washing such as greasy / spotted crockery and starch deposits may be rectified by using an alternative detergent (e.g. incorporating an oxidising agent to remove starch) and varying the temperature and amount of wash and rinse water.

Glass washing is often carried out separately because of the fragile nature of glass, the possibility of smearing and for beer glasses the 'head' of the beer which affects the foaming agents used in detergents. Some glass washing machines utilise a cleaning action in which revolving brushes clean the glass while it is held in place by hand. A sanitiser should be added and brushes must be kept clean and well maintained. On a larger scale fully automatic glass washers have high pressure water jets at appropriate temperatures to wash, rinse and disinfect.

Cooking vessels, pans, etc., must be washed separately from tableware. Detergents / scouring pads may be used although care must be taken in the cleaning of certain metal surfaces. Sodium hydrogen carbonate (bicarbonate) a degreasing agent can be used to remove grease from heavily soiled items.

9.5 Cleaning Work Surfaces / Counter Tops

These should be "cleaned as you go". All surfaces that touch food need to be cleaned properly but particular care is required with those in contact with high risk foods. Work surfaces in contact with raw foods should be cleaned thoroughly after use (including disinfection to destroy residual microorganisms thus minimising the risk of spreading pathogens). Similarly, work surfaces used for ready to eat foods should be cleaned after use and disinfected **before** use, even if they look clean. Studies have shown that work surfaces in kitchens may be used for a variety of purposes, by a range of people. There may be no way of knowing if someone has used the work surface for raw food or if it was cleaned appropriately. Therefore disinfecting immediately before use is an insurance against the chance contamination of ready to eat foods.

Step 1   Remove food debris / soil.

Step 2   Wash with clean hot water and detergent

Step 3   Rinse with clean hot water and clean cloth

Step 4   Apply suitable disinfectant and allow sufficient contact time

Step 5   Rinse off with fresh water and disposable paper towel

Step 6   Allow to air dry

On lightly soiled surfaces a sanitiser may be used and steps 2 and 4 omitted, alternatively sanitiser can be used in stages 2 and 4.

Chapter 10. CLEANING - AN ENFORCEMENT PERSPECTIVE

10.1 The Reasons for Cleanliness

The main purpose of ensuring high standards of cleanliness in food premises is to protect public health by ensuring that food does not become contaminated. The Food Safety Act 1990 makes it an offence to contaminate food so that it would be unreasonable to expect it to be used for human consumption in that state. In addition the Food Safety (General Food Hygiene) Regulations 1995 require the proprietor of a food business to identify any step in activities of the business which is critical to ensure food safety and to introduce effective controls at those points. There is, therefore, a clear obligation in law on the business proprietor to keep food premises clean wherever there is a risk to the food.

However, the proprietor's obligations do not end there. The Food Safety (General Food Hygiene) Regulations 1995 also stipulate that the premises must be kept clean and maintained in good repair and condition, be designed to allow proper cleaning and protect against the accumulation of dirt. In other words, it is not necessary for an enforcement officer to prove that any particular soil or dirt is a risk to health, it is simply necessary to prove that the dirt exists for an offence to have been committed. The regulations also require, for example, that floors and walls must be easy to clean and that ceilings and windows are constructed to prevent accumulations of dirt.

For the business proprietor these distinctions are very important, it is not acceptable simply to have clean premises, anything which jeopardises food safety, such as the potential contamination of food by dirty equipment or utensils, is prohibited. The requirement for cleanliness carries through from design and construction of the premises, to its maintenance and everyday use; there is even a requirement that, where necessary, facilities are provided and maintained to clean adequately work tools and equipment.

The proprietor will want to keep the premises clean not only because it is a legal requirement but because it makes good business sense. Clean and well-ordered premises tend to be more efficient, reduce wastage and help to give employees a sense that the business cares about its customers and staff. Dirty premises not only present health threats, they are frequently unpleasant to work in and engender a feeling of depression and gloom even before work commences. You must also ask yourself what impression dirty premises are likely to present to your customers.

10.2 What is "Clean"?

An enforcement officer visiting a food premises is charged with two primary functions. Firstly there is a requirement to identify any risks arising from the conduct of the business and to ensure that adequate controls are in place and, secondly, to identify any contraventions of the food safety legislation. Cleanliness will be assessed under both of these headings.

There is, however, the question as to what is meant by the word "clean"? In practice there is no single right answer since cleanliness itself will depend on circumstances. What may be acceptable in one situation, such as a raw vegetable store may be entirely inappropriate in another, such as a servery delivering high risk food to the customer. To assess whether or not premises and equipment are clean is to recognise that there are varying degrees of dirty. The assessment is frequently an application of informed common sense.

The enforcement officer will be making an assessment based on experience of that particular business sector, estimating what risk to health, if any, is posed by the premises or equipment and deciding whether all practical measures are being taken to minimise accumulations of dirt and soil. It is important to recognise that this assessment is increasingly being made using techniques such as microbial swabbing or ATP bioluminescence as well as the more traditional approach of only assessing visual cleanliness. These techniques are also available to the business proprietor, but their use should be approached with some caution as it can be easy to inadvertently misuse the equipment or to misinterpret the results. If in doubt it is always best to check with the manufacturers or the enforcement officer who will be pleased to advise you.

The enforcement officer will be looking for evidence that the premises are kept clean at all times and not just during the time of inspection. An experienced officer will be able to distinguish easily between dirt and spillages that have only just happened and those that have been there for some time, but a more confident assessment can be made if the premises have a written cleaning policy and schedule supplemented by a good recording system. A simple check of the records together with an inspection of the cleaning materials themselves is often sufficient to confirm that cleaning is a matter of routine and that it has been planned and executed as part of the everyday business of the premises. Assurances such as "We have just ran out of X or Y" tend to inspire little confidence, especially if the cleaning equipment is bone dry and the detergent or disinfectant container is covered with cobwebs.

The inspector will pay close attention to the suitability or otherwise of any chemicals used, unauthorised substitution is frequently a cause for suspicion, particularly if caustic chemicals or those which could cause a taint to be passed on to the food are used. The proprietor must recognise that there is no accepted colour coding of chemicals to act as a guide; there has been at least one instance where a green-coloured chemical has been substituted for an approved disinfectant simply on the grounds that it was cheaper than and the same colour as the original. In this case the substitution was of an authorised   disinfectant by a detergent with no disinfectant properties whatsoever, circumstances which may actually have contributed to the survival of germs leading to cross contamination and an eventual food poisoning outbreak.

In a similar way the smell of the chemical alone should not be used as a way of assessing its type. Just because many disinfectants are made to smell of pine should in no way be taken as an assurance that anything that smells of pine has automatically got disinfectant properties. Many detergents with no germ-killing power at all are made to smell of pine and mistaking one for the other can reduce dramatically the protection provided. All chemicals should be rigorously evaluated for their intended use and only approved chemicals, in the right concentrations, should be used. If there is any doubt the advice from the manufacturer or the suppliers should be sought.

10.3 When To Clean

As a general rule it is much easier to clean as you go rather than leave it until the end of the shift or the end of the day. This rule tends to break down however where it affects the smooth running of operations or where it is impractical   to keep stopping to remove the slightest unavoidable spillage. Examples of these could be where it is necessary to dismantle machinery to clean it or where spillage is practicably unavoidable, such as flour spillage during the mixing of bakery or confectionery products.

To assist the proprietor in determining when to clean it is perhaps useful to return to the consideration of why cleaning is being undertaken in the first place. If a particular operation generates the need for cleaning and there is any doubt about how quickly cleaning should commence, the proprietor should ask the question "Is there a food safety risk if this is not cleaned up immediately?", if the answer is "No" and cleaning would interrupt the flow of operations, it may be possible to leave the cleaning until later, but remember, if it can be cleaned sooner rather than later then it is better to do so. One final consideration should be any health and safety implications, a fat or grease spillage on the floor may not present any immediate food safety problem, but failure to clean immediately could present a very real safety hazard.

If you have any doubt about the frequency of cleaning it is probably easiest to ask the enforcement officer for an opinion directly, a telephone call to your local Environmental Health Department can save you a lot of worry and it should cost you nothing to get the expert advice you need. You should also be guided by the general principle that the longer spillages or accumulations are left to lie, the harder (and therefore more time-consuming and expensive) they become to remove. This can be a particular problem in catering when the attraction of going home after the end of a long shift and leaving the cleaning to the following day can be seductively appealing. This is usually an illusion in the longer term as the dirt takes much more effort to remove and leaving waste food lying around closed premises provides ample opportunity to attract pests, potentially leading to infestations.

It is recognised however that some cleaning procedures can only be undertaken when work has ceased or when the premises are not operating, such as during breaks or the end of the day. Such cleaning usually requires the dismantling or the moving of static equipment. The enforcement officer will also make allowances for any accumulations arising between such cleaning operations, but remember that at no time should accumulations pose a food safety risk and an inability to clean as you go solely due to poor premises layout or design or to old and unsuitable equipment is not acceptable.

10.4 Are There Any Cleaning Pitfalls?

The simple answer to this question is an emphatic "Yes". Most come under one (or both) of two categories, relating either to the direct health and safety of employees or to the passing on of risks to customers.

In the first instance the majority of hazards arise due to the inappropriate use of cleaning processed or chemicals. The most obvious pitfalls are perhaps the use of water in conjunction with electrical equipment, but other health and safety problems are associated with high pressure sprays, high temperature cleaning techniques (especially the use of steam) and a failure to follow manufacturer's instructions in cleaning procedures.

The latter include trying to dismantle and clean electrical equipment whilst it is still switched on, trying to delve around in equipment without switching off and dismantling it (pushing knives into electric toasters is a perennial problem) or trying to clean dangerous machinery (such as slicing equipment) without the appropriate personal safety equipment or adequate instruction. Remember, in the latter case, it is illegal to allow young people in any circumstances to clean certain equipment which is deemed to be dangerous, (your Health and Safety enforcement officer will advise you).

Another frequent failure is the inappropriate use of chemicals, often through mixing acid and alkaline chemicals together, or trying to improve their effectiveness by using them either neat or in concentrations far in excess of manufacturer's recommendations.   At best such use is frequently simply wasting money as the chemicals are rarely as effective as the user might anticipate, at worst the use can be directly hazardous to the employee and to work colleagues.

Proprietors need to recognise that commercial cleaning equipment and chemicals are usually potentially more dangerous than their domestic equivalents and new employees in particular may require detailed and specific training.

The second hazardous area involves those potential risks to the customer.   These include the use of inappropriate chemicals which can contaminate the food. Chemicals decanted into unsuitable containers where they become mistaken for food ingredients or other less dangerous chemicals, putting caustic chemicals into milk or soft drink containers for example happens more frequently than most people would think.   Other problems arise where cleaning tools damage equipment or cause breakages, leaving pieces of equipment free to contaminate food and injure consumers. Examples include the inappropriate use of powdered cleaners on delicate equipment and the inappropriate use of such equipment as wire brushes which can shed bristles which then get into the food.

Also in this secondary category there is the transfer of harmful bacteria and other microorganisms to the food through the incorrect use of cleaning equipment itself. In this category the use of a detergent instead of a disinfectant can lead to the spreading of germs to work surfaces and equipment. Whereas, in the normal course of events, the disinfectant would kill the germs, a detergent will not and wiping down with a damp cloth may present a visually clean surface, but could lead to residual microbial contamination.   This situation is made much worse in circumstances where the cleaning equipment itself is dirty, especially if it is contaminated with organic matter (particularly fat and grease) which serves simply as a breeding ground for germs which are then distributed liberally around the premises as "cleaning" takes place.

10.5 Which Types of Premises are a Problem?
Although different businesses present differing degrees of risk, with some notable exceptions such as slaughterhouses and similar premises, it is almost impossible to say

that one type of business invariably has the potential to create "dirtier" premises than another. Certain operations, such as the manufacture of bakery or confectionery products, can generate more dust and spillage than others, but good management and organisation will invariably overcome the usual difficulties associated with keeping food premises clean.

The most important considerations in determining whether or not premises are kept clean are the staff and the design and layout of both premises and equipment. Seasonal premises can be problematic because of the variability in staff quality. Frequently staff are inexperienced and can have little interest or commitment to the business itself and in these circumstances good management and clear, easily-understood rules are essential.

Tired, overworked and undervalued staff can also lead to problems. Long hours and late finishes often tempt staff to skimp on cleaning or to leave it until later, whilst a feeling of being undervalued can lead to indifference and slipshod performance. The manager or proprietor will need to conduct frequent checks and monitoring of performance, if a slide into dilapidation is to be avoided. For a single operator business the things to avoid are complacency or over-familiarity. The "open all hours" type premises can easily become cluttered if the owner is not careful and there is sometimes a tendency to save all sorts of oddments and curios in the belief that they will come in handy at some undefined time in the future.

Elderly, poorly converted premises and aged equipment frequently lead to difficulties. A badly-designed work area can take at least twice as long or more to clean and poor finishes can sometimes fail ever to look clean. Old equipment tends to be more difficult to clean than its modern counterparts and a machine which, on dismantling for cleaning, could cause personal injury, is likely to be left untouched by staff for as long as possible.

This is not to say that older premises or equipment should be avoided, but a well-considered assessment prior to opening will pay dividends. Staff time is expensive so someone who buys inferior products or finishes to try to save money can find it more expensive in the longer term as time spent on cleaning escalates.

10.6 What are the Main Problem Areas?

Cleaning equipment and materials are often overlooked and "cleaning" sometimes becomes simply a highly effective way of distributing germs across wide areas. The build up of dirt on scrubbing or sweeping brushes can be surprising and it is often the case that such dirt is unrecognised as few people ever look at the bristles or clean them. This can be a particular problem for equipment that is left wet after cleaning e.g. mops.

Those areas which are unlit and dark can be easily missed during cleaning a torch can be a good hygiene tool. Other inaccessible areas include light fittings, ceilings, deep cupboards, areas behind fixed equipment and underneath fittings all will become dirty if nobody can reach them to clean. This concern holds good for any "satellite" areas of the business, such as stores, which are set apart from the main activities and may consequently be visited less frequently.

Areas and equipment that are designated as "dirty", such as refuse stores, refuse bins and slop areas can become ignored or skimped during cleaning. The fact that they can become heavily contaminated and thereby be more resource intensive to clean doubtless encourages staff to avoid them if they are allowed to do so.

The heat exchangers of refrigerators and freezers are often found to be caked with dirt and dust not only is this unacceptable, it also means that the equipment is running less efficiently, is working harder to be effective and ultimately costs both more to run and wears out sooner. Extracter hoods for cookers, grease filters and extract ducting can become neglected; such items additionally present a significant fire hazard if not maintained correctly. Any ducting which is covered internally with grease and which catches alight is especially dangerous as it is difficult to put out and provides a very rapid route for fire to spread to other parts of the building.

The blades of commercial can openers can be neglected and the build up of waste food quickly decays leading to the inoculation of bacteria into subsequent cans during the opening process.

Lavatories and sanitary equipment require regular attention to keep them clean and free from germs. It is not surprising that many customers use the condition of the customer conveniences as a barometer to indicate standards of cleanliness elsewhere. What is surprising is the number of business operators who fail to recognise the fact.

Finally don't forget the staff themselves. They are potentially the most mobile distributor of dirt and germs in the food premises. Hand washing should be automatic before entering food premises after using the lavatory, after handling raw food (especially meats), after putting out the refuse or after hands have been in contact with ears, noses or mouths. The dirt you can see is a problem, the germs you cannot see are potentially lethal.

APPENDICES

Appendix 1 - Glossary of Terms

DEFINITIONS

Acidic	Substance with a pH less than 7
Aerobic Plate Count (APC)	A count of the number of bacteria that will grow at 30-37°C when aerobically incubated.
Anionic	Carrying or posessing a negative charge
Antiseptic	Literally means against infection - antimicrobial agent which can be used on the skin.
ATP	Adenosine triphosphate, a chemical found in all living cells. Levels of surface ATP can be used as a measure of cleanliness.
ADP	Adenosine diphosphate, the immediate precursor of ATP.
Adenylate kinase	The enzyme that converts ADP onto ATP.
Bacteriocide	Something which, under defined conditions, kills bacteria but not necessarily their spores.
Bacteriostatic	Something which, under defined conditions, is capable of preventing bacterial growth
Biocide	A chemical capable of destroying living cells.
Biofilm	No universally accepted definition within the food industry but it refers to an aggregation of microorganisms, adhering to a surface, surrounded by chemical material and moisture forming a matrix. Chemicals in the matrix include components of food debris and extracellular materials, including polymers, produced by the microorganisms. Liquid or atmosphere surrounding the biofilm is known as the planktonic phase.

How to Clean

Bioluminescence	Emission of light by an organism or a biochemical process. A technique for estimating the cleanliness of a surface based upon measuring light output. The amount of light emitted is proportional to the ATP present which in turn is a measure of surface cleanliness.
Buffer	Solution which maintains a relatively consistent pH.
Cationic	Carrying or possessing a positive charge
cfu	Colony forming units - the number of microroganisms (usually bacteria) that give rise to countable colonies
Chelating agent	Also known as sequestering agents, they are chemicals that hold unwanted inorganic ions (Calcium, Magnesium) in solution. They are important in hard water areas to prevent redeposition of salts back onto the surface being cleaned.
CIP	Cleaning in place, a programme of cleaning equipment without the need to disassemble or dismantle it.
Clean	Free of soil. The term can be used and interpreted differently to include:-

    visibly clean   - free from obvious soil or food

    chemically clean - free from food particles, soil and cleaning agents

    microbiologically - when the numbers and type of
    clean   microorganisms (microbial load) is at an acceptable level for use

Cleaning	Removal of soil from surfaces
Cleaning Schedule	Document containing information on how and when cleaning is to be carried out and what equipment and chemicals are used.

How to Clean

Cleaning Procedure	Detailed description of cleaning for each area or piece of equipment.
Cleaner	A person or a chemical used in cleaning.
Contamination	Objectionable material - chemical, physical or microbiological - present upon a food surface or product.
Control Measure	Actions or activities that can be used to eliminate hazards or reduce their impact or occurrence to acceptable levels.
Control Point	Any point or step in a process or procedure at which control can be achieved or applied
COP	Cleaning out of place, a programme of cleaning that requires equipment to be dismantled or moved.
Critical Control Point CCP	Any point or step at which control can be applied and a food safety hazard prevented, eliminated or reduced to an acceptable level.
Critical Limit	The value, of a monitored action, which separates acceptable from unacceptable
Cross Contamination	Process of contaminating a previously uncontaminated surface or food. It is of particular concern with microorganisms that have a low minimum infective dose e.g. *E.Coli* 0157, *Campylobacter*, SRSV.
Detergent	Substances which, on their own or in combination with others, in water, assist cleaning. They include surfactants, alkalis and acidic compounds.
Detergent / Disinfectant	Also known in the UK as sanitisers, they contain a mixture of chemicals enabling them, to a greater or lesser extent depending upon conditions, to both clean and disinfect surfaces.

Disinfection	The destruction or removal of microorganisms. At the end of disinfection the numbers and types of microorganisms should be acceptable and not present a risk. Disinfection is NOT sterilisation. In the USA sanitisation is often used synonomously with disinfection.
Emulsifying Agent	Something capable of keeping fat or oil dispersed in a suspension.
Fungicidal or Mycocidal	A substance which under defined conditions is capable of killing fungi.
Germicide	Substance capable of killing germs
Germ	Harmful microorganisms (synonomous with the term pathogen).
GRAM +ve	Those bacteria that stain blue / purple after the Gram stain procedure is applied.
GRAM -ve	Those bacteria that stain red after the Gram stain procedure is applied
GRAS	Generally regarded as safe.
HACCP	Hazard Analysis Critical Control Point. An internationally recognised approach to food safety management.
Hydrophilic	Literally water loving, having an affinity for water, water soluble.
Hydrophobic	Literally water fearing / hating, insoluble in water.
Monitoring	The planned series of observations or measurements of a named parameter, at an identified critical control point. The values obtained should be recorded and compared to the target level and permitted critical limits. The results of monitoring ideally should be obtained rapidly and in time to allow remedial action to be taken if the values are outside the critical limits.

How to Clean

Non-ionic	Lacking a charge, does not form ions in solution, electrically neutral.
Peptizing	The breakdown of insoluble proteins (polypeptides) into smaller fragments which can form a colloidal solution. Alkali cleaners can particularly break down proteins in this way.
pH	A scale from 0-14 that is a measure of the acidity or alkalinity of a substance.
Potable	Water suitable for human consumption
Psychrotrophic	Literally cold growing. Microorganism capable of growth at 5°C or below
Quats / QAC	Quaternary ammonium compounds, cationic detergents with antibacterial properties.
Sanitation	Cleaning process incorporating an additional element of disinfection (UK definition) anything that involves hygienic handling of foods (USA)
Sanitiser	Combined detergent / disinfectant (UK), disinfectant (USA)
Soil	Matter out of place, unwanted food residues, organic or inorganic matter remaining on the surface of equipment, dirt.
Sporicide	Capable of killing spores under defined conditions
Sterilisation	Complete removal of all microorganisms and their spores. Rarely, if ever, achieved or necessary in food industry.
Steriliser	A material that destroys all living microorganisms
Sterilant	A term incorrectly used to describe a disinfectant.
Surfactant	A wetting agent, substance that lowers the surface tension of a cleaning solution increasing the ability of that solution to penetrate the soil.

Target Level	Value of a parameter, at a critical control point, which has been shown to eliminate or control a hazard.
Validation	An element within the verification process which ensures that the initial design of the food safety system is accurate.
Verification	Methods, procedures or tests additional to those used in monitoring to determine if the HACCP system is in compliance with the HACCP plan and / or the HACCP plan needs modification or review. Microbiological testing can often be useful in verification.
Water Hardness	Describing the level of salts in solution, water containing an elevated level of salts can reduce the efficacy of cleaning.

Appendix 2 - Cause and Effect Analysis

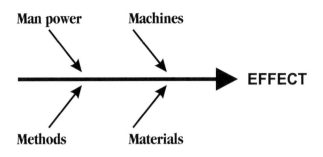

Cause and effect analysis is a technique often used by quality circles and provides an additional structure to brainstorming by grouping ideas together. The effect or problem (e.g. contamination) is represented by a vertical or horizontal arrow or spine, potential principal causes are identified arrows entering the spine. In turn each principal arrow can have secondary arrows representing sub causes. The end result is a diagram that lists all the causes of a problem with the appearance of a fish bone. The prinicipal causes are often considered under the heading of the 4M's. These stand for:-

Man power	Skills, training, attitudes, knowledge
Method	Procedures, inspections
Machines	Processing, engineering
Materials	Attributes of the product and its components

Once a comprehensive fishbone diagram has been constructed, the team attempts to verify the possible causes, identify the most important and prioritise action.

Cause and effect Analysis Applied to problem Cleaning

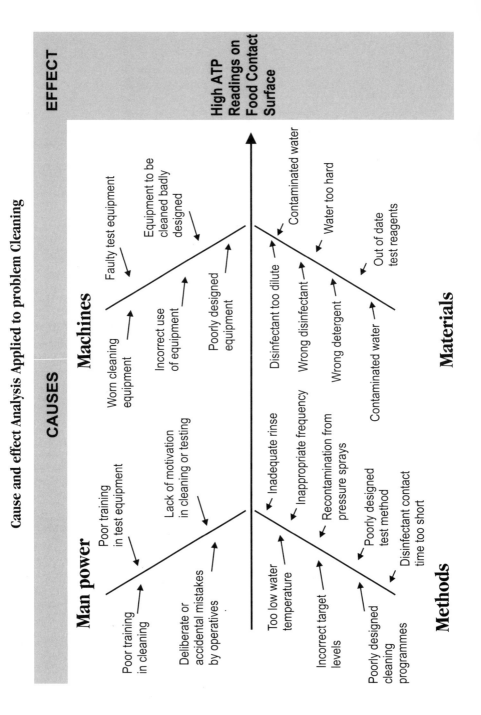

EFFECT

High ATP Readings on Food Contact Surface

CAUSES

Machines

Faulty test equipment

Equipment to be cleaned badly designed

Worn cleaning equipment

Incorrect use of equipment

Poorly designed equipment

Man power

Poor training in test equipment

Lack of motivation in cleaning or testing

Poor training in cleaning

Deliberate or accidental mistakes by operatives

Contaminated water

Water too hard

Out of date test reagents

Disinfectant too dilute

Wrong disinfectant

Wrong detergent

Contaminated water

Materials

Inadequate rinse

Inappropriate frequency

Recontamination from pressure sprays

Poorly designed test method

Disinfectant contact time too short

Too low water temperature

Incorrect target levels

Poorly designed cleaning programmes

Methods

Appendix 3 - Example Cleaning Documentation

Example of a Shamrock Fisheries cleaning schedule in place for a process area

CLEANING SCHEDULE
Area: *Process Area*

Item	Freq	Doc	Rev
INTAKE BELT	Daily, Weekly	Process IBL	1
WASH TANK & SALTING	Daily	Process TNK	1
DISCHARGE BELT	Daily, Weekly	Process DBL	1
GRADER - TABLES	Daily, Weekly	Process GRD	1
WALLS	Weekly	Process WLS	1
FLOORS	Weekly	Process FLR	1

Examples of a cards used in Shamrock Fisheries cleaning procedure

---

CLEANING METHOD

h

FACTORY PROCESSES ITEM: Intake Belt

CLEANING EQUIPMENT TO USE:

☐ Eqpt Buckets	☑ Envir. Buckets	☑ Squeegees
☐ Eqpt Brushes	☑ Envir. Brushes	☑ Low Pressure Hose
☐ Eqpt Cloths	☑ Envir. Cloths	☑ High Pressure Hose
	☑ Envir. Long-Handled Brushes	

CLEANING CHEMICALS TO USE:

FLOORKLENZ @ 2 %
POWERFOAM @ 3 %

Chemical (eg QAC):
Makeup (eg
ppm Free Cl);

CLEANING METHOD TO USE:

=> Erect "Cleaning In Place" signs at the entrances to the process area.

=> Foam the conveyer whilst Still moving, using 3% Powerfoam and a high pressure foaming lance and hot water if possible. Take care not to spray other equipment, any electrical connections, sockets or conduits.

=> Turn the conveyer off and leave for 20 minutes to allow the foam to work.

=> Turn the conveyer back on and rinse off the foam using a low pressure hose. Ensure the hose is rewound and placed in detergent sanitiser after use.

=> With the conveyer turned off and isolated, the belt should be slackened by the engineering department to allow further cleaning.

=> Scrub any stubborn marks and between each slat with a 2% solution of Floorklenz made up with hot water, and a small environmental brush.

=> When finished, allow the engineers to tighten the belt. Start the belt and hose down once more using the low pressure hose.

=> Squeegee any remaining water down the nearest convenient drain and remove the cleanig signs.

Visual	Visibly Clean
ATP	<500 RLUs
Micro CFU	<250/100cm^2

CLEANING METHOD

j

FACTORY PROCESSES ITEM: Wash Tank

CLEANING EQUIPMENT TO USE:

- ☑ Eqpt Buckets
- ☑ Eqpt Brushes
- ☑ Eqpt Cloths
- ☐ Envir. Buckets
- ☐ Envir. Brushes
- ☐ Envir. Cloths
- ☐ Envir. Long-Handled Brushes
- ☑ Squeegees
- ☑ Low Pressure Hose
- ☑ High Pressure Hose

CLEANING CHEMICALS TO USE:

STERICLEAN @ 2%
POWERFOAM @ 3%

Chemical (eg QAC):
Makeup (eg
ppm Free Cl);

CLEANING METHOD TO USE:

=> Erect "Cleaning In Place" signs either side of the wash tank area.

=> Drain the tank of water rinsing as much soiling away as possible with the low pressure hose, as the tank drains.

=> Foam the internal and external surfaces of the tank using 3% Powerfoam and a high pressure foaming lance and hot water if possible. Take care not to spray other equipment, any electrical connections, sockets or conduits.

=> Leave for 20 minutes to allow the foam to work.

Rinse off the foam using a low pressure hose. Ensure the hose is rewound and placed in detergent sanitiser after use.

=> Scrub. any stubborn marks and around the intake and discharge belt areas with a 2% solution of Stericlean made up with hot water, and a small equipment brush There is no need to rinse following this activity as the detergent has residual sterilising properties.

=> Squeegee any remaining water down the nearest convenient drain and remove the cleaning signs.
=> Refill the tank

Visual	Visibly Clean
ATP	<500 RLUs
Micro CFU	<250/100cm^2

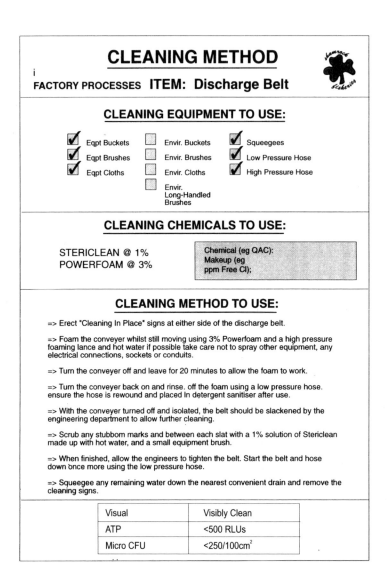

CLEANING METHOD

i

FACTORY PROCESSES ITEM: Discharge Belt

CLEANING EQUIPMENT TO USE:

- ☑ Eqpt Buckets
- ☑ Eqpt Brushes
- ☑ Eqpt Cloths
- ☐ Envir. Buckets
- ☐ Envir. Brushes
- ☐ Envir. Cloths
- ☐ Envir. Long-Handled Brushes
- ☑ Squeegees
- ☑ Low Pressure Hose
- ☑ High Pressure Hose

CLEANING CHEMICALS TO USE:

STERICLEAN @ 1%
POWERFOAM @ 3%

Chemical (eg QAC):
Makeup (eg
ppm Free Cl);

CLEANING METHOD TO USE:

=> Erect "Cleaning In Place" signs at either side of the discharge belt.

=> Foam the conveyer whilst still moving using 3% Powerfoam and a high pressure foaming lance and hot water if possible take care not to spray other equipment, any electrical connections, sockets or conduits.

=> Turn the conveyer off and leave for 20 minutes to allow the foam to work.

=> Turn the conveyer back on and rinse. off the foam using a low pressure hose. ensure the hose is rewound and placed In detergent sanitiser after use.

=> With the conveyer turned off and isolated, the belt should be slackened by the engineering department to allow further cleaning.

=> Scrub any stubborn marks and between each slat with a 1% solution of Stericlean made up with hot water, and a small equipment brush.

=> When finished, allow the engineers to tighten the belt. Start the belt and hose down once more using the low pressure hose.

=> Squeegee any remaining water down the nearest convenient drain and remove the cleaning signs.

Visual	Visibly Clean
ATP	<500 RLUs
Micro CFU	<250/100cm^2

Appendix 4 - Examples of Validation Records

Specific Trials Programme - EXAMPLE
Terms of Reference - **CLEANING EFFECTIVENESS**
Scope - **Microbiological**
Hazard Survival of **organisms**
No. Samples / Observations: 5 samples take with observations via checklists & ATP

Validation Date: **1.1.2000**
Control Measures: **Cleaning and Sanitation**
Responsible: **JH**

Area Risk: **High**
Source: **Personnel**
Factory Area: **Trimming**

Process Step	Observations / Sample No.	Time Sample / Observation Taken & Description	Equipment Required	Performance Targets	Actual Results	Reference Material	Validated Target Limit
Trimming	1 5 samples and prep agar plates	1700 - 10cm area taken with 5 swabs	Incubator	No gross debris Condition of contact surface at end of production	1000,000 CFUs ATP 20,000 RLUs	Hygiene management system Microbial Data	ATP <200RLUs CFU < 200/100 cm^2
Trimming	2 5 samples and prep agar plates	1715 - surface has been rinsed	Incubator	Removal of surface soil and debris from contact surface	10,000 CFUs ATP 1000 RLUs	Hygiene management system Microbial Data	ATP <200RLUs CFU < 200/100 cm^2
Trimming	3 5 samples and prep agar plates	1745 - surface has been clean and sanitised	Incubator	Removal of surface soil and contaminants look visibly clean. No chemical residue and damp surface	100 CFUs ATP 150 RLUs	Hygiene management system Microbial Data	ATP <200RLUs CFU < 200/100 cm^2
Trimming	4 5 samples and prep agar plates	0730 1.1.2000 surface prior to production	Incubator	No surface contaminants	100 CFUs ATP 150 RLUs	Hygiene management system Microbial Data	ATP <200RLUs CFU < 200/100 cm^2

Validation Reference Material Sources   VAL001a   Area Risk: **High**

Source: **Personnel**

Process Step: **Trimming**   Hazard **Cleaning & Sanitation**   Factory Area: **Trimming**

Control Measures: **Prevention of growth of Microflora**

Current Target / Tolerance Limit: **50 cfu / ml (200 RLU)**

Information Source	Reference Material (Title/Year Volume/Pages)	Reference Source (Paper/Article)	Recommended Target Limit/ Tolerance	Are Data/methods applicable to the product?		Current Limits Accceptable		Further Validation Required		If yes, state reason for not validating	If no, state reason for not validating
				Yes	No	Yes	No	Yes	No		
Trade association IFST / GMP	ATP levels in Dairy Ind Vol 33 (1998) 55 - 76	IFST Journal	30 cfu/ml 250 RLU's		N				N		Currently within current Standards
Trade reference material Journals, Magazines	Vol. 9 No. 3 (1998) 11	Int. Food Hygiene	60 cfu/ml 250 RLU's	Y		Y			N		Currently Within Recommended Data set
Legislative Material	Govnt Report (1998) 100 - 146	Hygiene & Sanitation	30 cfu/ml 250 RLU's	Y			N	Y		Trial Design Data Research Product spec	
Industry Codes of Practise	Newsletter (1995) p 4-6	Crab Producers Assoc.	50 cfu/ml 250 RLU's	Y		Y			N		Monitored through Verification

Appendix 5 - Detailed Example of Investment Appraisal

Management may be faced with decisions about buying capital items (Capital Expenditure = CAPEX). Investment appraisal will assist the manager in making those decisions - the following brief descriptions are intended to assist the reader in understanding the information the software tool described in section 8 produces for the financial team to assess.

The three main methods of investment appraisal are as follows:

- Payback period
- Accounting rate of return
- Net present value

Payback period

For example a foam applicator is purchased for £4,000 - the estimated savings in labour are as follows:

yr. 1	1500
yr. 2	1500
yr. 3	1000

In this case the payback period is three years - if the labour saving had continued at £1,500 per annum then payback would have occurred at some point within year 3 and can be measured more accurately if required. Payback is based on cashflow rather than profit and is simple to calculate and is useful to businesses were cashflow is tight. Payback does not consider the "time value" of money i.e. £1 in 1999 may only be worth 90p in 2000. The method also ignores future profits only identifying the point at which the machine pays for itself.

The Accounting Rate of Return (ARR)

This takes into account future profit e.g the firm purchase a new CIP system for £100,000- cash flows generated by investment:

yr. 1	£40,000
yr. 2	£50,000
yr. 3	£40,000
yr. 4	£30,000
total	£160,000

Accounting rate of return is calculated using this formula

ARR= (total profit/no of years) / cost of investment x 100

£160,000 - £100,000/ 4 / £100,000 x 100
£15,000/ 100,000 x 100= 15%

This means that for every £ invested we receive £1 plus 15 p profit.

This method allows the measure of profit generated by the purchase as opposed to the pay back period. Exact payback may be useful to compare investments with similar rates of return. Finally we need to consider the time value of money which will be achieved by projecting the future value of money at a predicted interest rate.

Net present value

Time value of Money Discounted Cash Flows project the future value of money and by looking up discount factors for given interest rates then the effect of time and a projected interest rate money value can be predicted.

The method used is Net Present Value which compares the inflow of cash with the outflow. The inflow of cash over the period of the investment must be discounted at the agreed rates - e.g. the purchase of a new cleaning system for £5,000.

Estimated Savings	Discounted Factor for 16% Interest	Actual Value/£
2000	.862	1724.00
2500	.743	1857.50
2500	.641	1602.50
	Total Inflow	£5184.00

Positive cash inflow of £184 allowing for depreciation of the money (£5184-£5000- invested).

This method accounts for future profits beyond break even and enables the management to assess the time value of money. Although the interest rate/ cost of capital is assumed to remain constant the software tool can enable variations to be assessed. Cash inflows at future dates are difficult to accurately predict.

Cost of Capital - Investment risk

The business must assess available interest rates, investment opportunities and risk of investment. If the loan rate from the bank is 5% above base rate (which may be 10%) then the cost to the business is 15% to borrow the money. Additionally the business may earn 14% from a specific investment opportunity. The risk of a given investment in new plant must also be assessed - for example the new CIP plant for £100,000 may not pay back as quickly as claimed or staff training and maintenance costs are difficult to predict. This may result in the business adding a further 5% to the cost of capital for this investment to cover the risk. If the investment does not return profit on the 20% level then the investment may not proceed.

Some basic elements of costing and of investment analysis which will assist the manager in making decisions about improvement or investment in new facilities. The reader is directed to selected textbooks on costing and financial analysis in Appendix.

Appendix 6 - Extract from Environmental Technology Best Practice Programme (1998)

Guidance on Reducing Cleaning Costs

- Find out your company water costs, annually and per m3
- Find out your company effluent disposal cost, annually and per m3
- Evaluate how much of the site water consumption is used for cleaning
- Identify the overall cost of cleaning
- Identify the major users of water for cleaning purposes
- Consider installation of water meters for any major users and monitor consumption
- Implement low and no cost opportunities for reducing cleaning costs, ensure that hygiene standards will not be adversely affected
- Implement dry clean-up methods
- Educate managers, production and cleaning personnel on how to improve cleaning efficiency and reduce costs, emphasise financial and environmental benefits
- Investigate other project opportunities for improved cleaning efficiency to assess which are economically , technically and practically feasible while ensuring hygiene standards are met
- Consider using alternative cleaning methods
- Implement measures to improve cleaning cost effectively
- Review and feed back

Source adapted from Ref. 8

Appendix 7 - CEN Tests

Tests for cleaning chemicals to assess effectiveness are being developed by working groups.

CEN tests Phase 1 are covered by:
BS EN 1040: 1997 Basic Bactericidal Activity
BS EN 1275: 1997 Basic Fungicidal Activity

Phase 2 - Step 1 is covered by
BS EN 1276: 1997
BS EN 1650: 1998
Step 2 is to be a surface test.

Phase 2, Step 1, BS EN 1276: 1997
Two soil levels are defined:
"Clean" 0.03% Bovine albumin
"Dirty" 1.00% Bovine albumin

The test bacteria used are:
Escherichia coli ATCC10536
Enterococcus hirae NCIMB8191
Pseudomonas aeruginosa NCIMB10421
Staphylococcus aureus ATCC6538

Copies of the standards may be obtained through the British Standards Institute.

Source adapted from ref. 23

Appendix 8 - Useful References

1. Armstrong, G. (1999), Towards Integrated Hygiene and Food Safety Management Systems: The Hygineomic Approach. . Hygienomics - The Global Hygiene Forum. Helsinki, May.

2. Chesworth, N. - Editor. (1997). Food Hygiene Auditing. Blackie Academic & Professional.

3. Davidson, C.A., Griffith, C. J., Peters, A. C. and Fielding, L.M. (1999). An evaluation of two methods for monitoring surface cleanliness ATP Bioluminescence and Traditional Hygiene Swabbing. Luminescence 13: 1-5.

4. Dillon, M & Griffith, C. J. (1996) How to HACCP 2nd Edition. M. D. Associates.

5. Dillon, M. & Griffith, C. J. (1997) How to Audit - Verifying Food Control Systems. M. D. Associates.

6. Dillon, M. (1999). Cost Effective Food Control. The Global Hygiene Forum. Helsinki, May.

7. Elvers, K., Peters, A. C. and Griffith, C. J. (1998). Biofilms and their Risk to the Food Industry. Conference Proceedings Microbial Control in the Food Industry. Cardiff. July

8. Environmental Technology Best Practice Programme (1998). Reducing the Cost of Cleaning in the Food and Drink Industry.

9. Food Safety Act 1990. Code of Practice 9. Food Hygiene Inspection. HMSO 1991

10. Griffith, C. J., Davidson, C., Peters, A. C. and Fielding, L.M. (1997). Towards a strategic cleaning assessment programme: hygiene monitoring and ATP luminometry, an option appraisal. Food Science and Technology Today. 11:15-24

11. Gibson, H., Taylor, J.H., Hall, K.E., Holah, J.T. (1999). Effectiveness of cleaning techniques used in the food industry in terms of the removal of bacterial biofilms.

12. Henkel-Ecolab GmbH & Co.OHG, P.O. Box 13 04 06, D-40554, Dusseldorf. Tel. 49211/9893203

13. Hobbs B. C. & Roberts, D. (1989). Food Poisoning & Food Hygiene 5th Edition. Edward Arnold

14. ICMSF (1988). HACCP in Microbiological Safety & Quality. Blackwell Scientific Publications.

15. Innovise Software Ltd., Stubbers Farm, Mountnessing Road, Blackmore, Essex. CM4 0NX
Tel. +44 (0) 1277 822511

16. Institute of Food Science & Technology. (1993). List of Codes of Practice Applicable to Food.

17. International Food Hygiene various copies are very useful sources of information.

18. Jay, J. M. (1996). Modern Food Microbiology 4th Edition. Chapman & Hall, London.

19. Jukes, D. J. (1993). Food Legislation of the UK 3rd Edition. Butterworth-Heinemann Ltd.

20. Marriott, N.G. (1999). Principle of Food Sanitation. 4th Edition Aspen Publications.

21. Mortimore, S. & Wallace, C. (1998). HACCP - A practical approach. Chapman & Hall. London.

22. Peters, A. C., Williams, N., Griffith, C. J., Fielding, L. and Davidson, C. (1998) Validating ATP Bioluminescence in Hygiene Monitoring. Conference Proceedings Microbial Control in the Food Industry. Cardiff. July.

23. Rigarlsford, J. (1999). Developments in Cleaning and Disinfection. The Society of Food Hygiene Technology, Coventry University Symposium, 17th June 1999.

24. Shapton, D. A. & Shapton, N. F. - Editors. (1993). Heinz - Principles & Practices for the Safe Processing of Foods. Butterworth-Heinemann Ltd.

25. Sprenger, R. A. (1998). Hygiene for Management 8th Edition. Highfield Publications.